SYMBIOSIS the benjamin cummings custom laboratory program for the biological sciences

Microbiology Laboratory Experiments

PEARSON
Custom
Publishing

PEARSON
Benjamin
Cummings

Director of Database Publishing: Michael Payne
Executive Marketing Manager: Nathan L. Wilbur
Operations Manager: Eric M. Kenney
Development Editor: Katherine Thompson
Production Manager: Jennifer Berry
Cover Designers: Shelley Kondrat and Eric Tamlin

Cover Art: Courtesy of Michael R. Martin, Darryl Johnson, and Photodisc.

Pyrex, pHydrion, Chem3D Plus, Apple, Macintosh, Chemdraw, Hypercard, graphTool, Corning, Teflon, Mel-Temp, Rotaflow, Tygon, Spec20, and LambdaII UV/Vis are registered trademarks.

Chem3D Plus is a registered trademark of the Cambridge Soft Corp.

The information, illustration, and/or software contained in this book, and regarding the above mentioned programs, are provided "as is," without warranty of any kind, express or implied, including without limitation any warranty concerning the accuracy, adequacy, or completeness of such information. Neither the publisher, the authors, nor the copyright holders shall be responsible for any claims attributable to errors, omissions, or other inaccuracies contained in this book. Nor shall they be liable for direct, indirect, special, incidental, or consequential damages arising out of the use of such information or material.

The authors and publisher believe that the lab experiments described in this publication, when conducted in conformity with the safety precautions described herein and according to the school's laboratory safety procedures, are reasonably safe for the students for whom this manual is directed. Nonetheless, many of the described experiments are accompanied by some degree of risk, including human error, the failure or misuse of laboratory or electrical equipment, mismeasurement, spills of chemicals, and exposure to sharp objects, heat, body fluids, blood or other biologics. The authors and publisher disclaim any liability arising from such risks in connections with any of the experiments contained in this manual. If students have questions or problems with materials, procedures, or instructions on any experiment, they should always ask their instructor for help before proceeding.

This special edition published in cooperation with Pearson Custom Publishing.

Printed in the United States of America.

Please visit our web site at *www.pw-bc.com/symbiosis*

Attention bookstores: For permission to return unused stock, call 800-428-4266.

ISBN-13: 978-0-536-09759-0   ISBN-10: 0-536-09759-3

PEARSON CUSTOM PUBLISHING
501 Boylston St., Suite 900
Boston, MA 02116

Laboratory Safety:
General Guidelines

1. Notify your instructor immediately if you are pregnant, color blind, allergic to any insects or chemicals, taking immunosuppressive drugs, or have any other medical condition (such as diabetes, immunologic defect) that may require special precautionary measures in the laboratory.

2. Upon entering the laboratory, place all books, coats, purses, backpacks, etc. in designated areas, not on the bench tops.

3. Locate and, when appropriate, learn to use exits, fire extinguisher, fire blanket, chemical shower, eyewash, first aid kit, broken glass container, and cleanup materials for spills.

4. In case of fire, evacuate the room and assemble outside the building.

5. Do not eat, drink, smoke, or apply cosmetics in the laboratory.

6. Confine long hair, loose clothing, and dangling jewelry.

7. Wear shoes at all times in the laboratory.

8. Cover any cuts or scrapes with a sterile, waterproof bandage before attending lab.

9. Wear eye protection when working with chemicals.

10. Never pipet by mouth. Use mechanical pipeting devices.

11. Wash skin immediately and thoroughly if contaminated by chemicals or microorganisms.

12. Do not perform unauthorized experiments.

13. Do not use equipment without instruction.

14. Report *all* spills and accidents to your instructor immediately.

15. Never leave heat sources unattended.

16. When using hot plates, note that there is no visible sign that they are hot (such as a red glow). Always assume that hot plates are hot.

17. Use an appropriate apparatus when handling hot glassware.

18. Keep chemicals away from direct heat or sunlight.

19. Keep containers of alcohol, acetone, and other flammable liquids away from flames.

20. Do not allow any liquid to come into contact with electrical cords. Handle electrical connectors with dry hands. Do not attempt to disconnect electrical equipment that crackles, snaps, or smokes.

21. Upon completion of laboratory exercises, place all materials in the disposal areas designated by your instructor.

22. Do not pick up broken glassware with your hands. Use a broom and dustpan and discard the glass in designated glass waste containers; never discard with paper waste.

23. Wear disposable gloves when working with blood, other body fluids, or mucous membranes. Change gloves after possible contamination and wash hands immediately after gloves are removed.

24. The disposal symbol indicates that items that may have come in contact with body fluids should be placed in your lab's designated container. It also refers to liquid wastes that should not be poured down the drain into the sewage system.

25. Leave the laboratory clean and organized for the next student.

26. Wash your hands with liquid or powdered soap prior to leaving the laboratory.

27. The biohazard symbol indicates procedures that may pose health concerns.

The caution symbol points out instruments, substances, and procedures that require special attention to safety. These symbols appear throughout this manual.

Measurement Conversions

Metric to American Standard

Length

1 mm = 0.039 inches

1 cm = 0.394 inches

1 m = 3.28 feet

1 m = 1.09 yards

Volume

1 mL = 0.0338 fluid ounces

1 L = 4.23 cups

1 L = 2.11 pints

1 L = 1.06 quarts

1 L = 0.264 gallons

Mass

1 mg = 0.0000353 ounces

1 g = 0.0353 ounces

1 kg = 2.21 pounds

Temperature

American Standard to Metric

Length

1 inch = 2.54 cm

1 foot = 0.305 m

1 yard = 0.914 m

1 mile = 1.61 km

Volume

1 fluid ounce = 29.6 mL

1 cup = 237 mL

1 pint = 0.474 L

1 quart = 0.947 L

1 gallon = 3.79 L

Mass

1 ounce = 28.3 g

1 pound = 0.454 kg

To convert temperature:

$$°C = \frac{5}{9}(F - 32)$$

$$°F = \frac{9}{5}C + 32$$

°F	°C	
230	110	
220		
210	100	Water boils
200		
190	90	
180		
170	80	
160		
150	70	
140	60	
130		
120	50	
110		
100	40	
98.6°F		37.0°C
Normal human body temperature		Normal human body temperature
90	30	
80		
70	20	
60		
50	10	
40		
30	0	Water freezes
20		
10	−10	
0	−20	
−10		
−20	−30	
−30		
−40	−40	

Centimeters	Inches
20	8
19	7
18	
17	
16	6
15	
14	5
13	
12	
11	4
10	
9	
8	3
7	
6	2
5	
4	
3	1
2	
1	
0	0

Contents

Introduction

Life would not long remain possible in the absence of microbes.

LOUIS PASTEUR

Welcome to microbiology! Microorganisms are all around us, and as Pasteur pointed out over a century ago, they play vital roles in the ecology of life on Earth. In addition, some microorganisms provide important commercial benefits through their use in the production of chemicals (including antibiotics) and certain foods. Microorganisms are also major tools in basic research in the biological sciences. Finally, as we all know, some microorganisms cause disease—in humans, other animals, and plants.

In this course, you will have firsthand experience with a variety of microorganisms. You will learn the techniques required to identify, study, and work with them. Before getting started, you will find it helpful to read through the suggestions on the next few pages.

Suggestions to Help You Begin

1. Science has a vocabulary of its own. New terms will be introduced in **boldface** throughout this manual. To develop a working vocabulary, make a list of these new terms and their definitions.
2. Because microbes are not visible without a microscope, common names have not been given to them. The word *microbe*, now in common use, was introduced in 1878 by Charles Sedillot. The microbes used in the exercises in this manual are referred to by their *scientific names*. The names will be unfamiliar at first, but do not let that deter you. Practice saying them aloud. Most scientific names are taken from Latin and Greek roots. If you become familiar with these roots, the names will be easier to remember.
3. Microbiology usually provides the first opportunity undergraduate students have to experiment with *living organisms*. Microbes are relatively easy to grow and lend themselves to experimentation. Because there is variability in any population of living organisms, not all the experiments will "work" as the lab manual says. The following exercise will illustrate what we mean:

    Write a description of *Homo sapiens* for a visitor from another planet: _____
    _____
    _____
    _____
    _____
    _____
    _____

After you have finished, look around you. Do all your classmates fit the description exactly? Probably not. Moreover, the more detailed you make your description, the less conformity you will observe. During lab, you will make a detailed description of an organism and probably find that this description does not match your reference exactly.

4. Microorganisms must be cultured or grown to complete most of the exercises in this manual. Cultures will be set up during one laboratory period and will be examined for growth in the next laboratory period. Accurate record keeping is therefore essential. Mark the steps in each exercise with a bright color or a bookmark so you can return to complete your Laboratory Report on that exercise. *Accurate records* and *good organization* of laboratory work will enhance your enjoyment and facilitate your learning.
5. *Observing* and *recording* your results carefully are the most important parts of each exercise. Ask yourself the following questions for each experiment:
    What did the results indicate?
    Are they what I expected? If not, what happened?
6. If you do not master a technique, try it again. In most instances, you will need to use the technique again later in the course.
7. Be sure you can answer the questions that are asked in the Procedure for each exercise. These questions are included to reinforce important points that will ensure a successful experiment.
8. Finally, carefully study the general procedures and safety precautions that follow.

General Procedures in Microbiology

In many ways, working in a microbiology laboratory is like working in the kitchen. As some famous chefs have said:

Our years of teaching cookery have impressed upon us the fact that all too often a debutant cook will start in enthusiastically on a new dish without ever reading the recipe first. Suddenly an ingredient, or a process, or a time sequence will turn up, and there is astonishment, frustration, and even disaster. We therefore urge you, however much you have cooked, always to read the recipe first, even if the dish is familiar to you. . . . We have not given estimates for the time of preparation, as some people take half an hour to slice three pounds of mushrooms, while others take five minutes.*

From *Laboratory Experiments in Microbiology,* Eighth Edition, Ted R. Johnson and Christine L. Case. Copyright © 2006 by Pearson Education, Inc. Published by Benjamin Cummings, Inc. All rights reserved.

1. Read the laboratory exercises *before* coming to class.
2. *Plan* your work so that all experiments will be completed during the assigned laboratory period. A good laboratory student, like a good cook, is one who can do more than one procedure at a time—that is, one who is efficient.
3. Use only the *required* amounts of materials, so that everyone can do the experiment.
4. *Label* all of your experiments with your name, date, and lab section.
5. Even though you will do most exercises with another student, you must become familiar with all parts of each exercise.
6. Keep *accurate* notes and records of your procedures and results so that you can refer to them for future work and tests. Many experiments are set up during one laboratory period and observed for results in the next laboratory period. Your notes are essential to ensure that you perform all the necessary steps and observations.
7. *Demonstrations* will be included in some of the exercises. Study the demonstrations and learn the content.
8. Let your instructor know if you are color-blind; many techniques require discrimination of colors.
9. Keep your cultures current; discard old experiments.
10. *Clean up* your work area when you are finished. Leave the laboratory clean and organized for the next student. Remember:

    Stain and reagent bottles should be returned to their original locations.

    Slides should be washed and put back into the box clean.

    All markings on glassware (e.g., Petri plates and test tubes) should be removed before putting glassware into the marked autoclave trays.

    Glass Petri plates should be placed agar-side down in marked autoclave containers.

    Swabs and pipettes should be placed in the appropriate disinfectant jars or biohazard containers.

    Disposable plasticware should be placed in marked autoclave containers.

    Used paper towels should be discarded.

Biosafety

The most important element for managing microorganisms is strict adherence to standard microbiological practices and techniques, which you will learn during this

course. There are four biosafety levels (BSLs) for working with live microorganisms; each BSL consists of combinations of laboratory practices and techniques, safety equipment, and laboratory facilities. See Table 1 on page xiii. Each combination is specifically appropriate for the operations performed, the documented or suspected routes of transmission of the microorganisms, and the laboratory function or activity.

Biosafety Level 1 represents a basic level of containment that relies on standard microbiological practices with no specific facilities other than a sink for hand washing. When standard laboratory practices are not sufficient to control the hazard associated with a particular microorganism, additional measures may be used.

Biosafety Level 2 includes hand washing, and an autoclave must be available. Precautions must be taken for handling and disposing of contaminated needles or sharp instruments. BSL 2 is appropriate when working with human body fluids. A lab coat should be worn.

Biosafety Level 3 is used in laboratories where work is done with pathogens that can be transmitted by the respiratory route. BSL 3 requires special facilities with self-closing, double doors and sealed windows.

Biosafety Level 4 is applicable for work with pathogens that may be transmitted via aerosols and for which there is no vaccine or safety. The BSL 4 facility is generally a separate building with specialized ventilation and waste management systems to prevent release of live pathogens to the environment.

Which biosafety level is your lab? _____

Specific Hazards in the Laboratory

 Procedures marked with this safety icon should be performed carefully to minimize risk of exposure to chemicals or fire.

Alcohol

Keep containers of alcohol away from open flames.

Glassware Not Contaminated with Microbial Cultures

1. If you break a glass object, sweep up the pieces with a broom and dustpan. Do not pick up pieces of broken glass with your bare hands.
2. Place broken glass in one of the containers marked for this purpose. The one exception to this rule concerns broken mercury thermometers; consult your instructor if you break a mercury thermometer.

---

*J. Child, L. Bertholle, and S. Beck. *Mastering the Art of French Cooking*, Vol. 1. New York: Knopf, 1961.

Table 1

Biosafety Levels

Biosafety Level	Practices	Safety Equipment (Primary Barriers)	Facilities (Secondary Barriers)
1	Standard microbiological practices	None required	Open benchtop sink
2	BSL1 plus • Limited access • Biohazard warning signs • "Sharps" precautions • Safety manual of waste-decontamination policies	Lab coat; gloves, as needed	BSL1 plus autoclave
3	BSL 2 plus • Controlled access • Decontamination of clothing before laundering	BSL 2 plus protective lab clothing; enter and leave lab through clothing changing and shower rooms	BSL 2 plus self-closing, double-door access
4	BSL 3 plus • Separate building	BSL 3 plus full-body air-supplied, positive pressure personnel suit	BSL 3 plus separate building and decontamination facility

Electrical Equipment

1. The basic rule to follow is this: Electricity and water don't mix. Do not allow water or any water-based solution to come into contact with electrical cords or electrical conductors. Make sure your hands are dry when you handle electrical connectors.
2. If your electrical equipment crackles, snaps, or begins to give off smoke, do not attempt to disconnect it. Call your instructor immediately.

Fire

1. If *gas burns* from a leak in the burner or tubing, turn off the gas.
2. If you have a *smoldering sleeve*, run water on the fabric.
3. If you have a *very small fire*, the best way to put it out is to smother it with a towel or book (not your hand). Smother the fire quickly.
4. If a *larger fire* occurs, such as in a wastebasket or sink, use one of the fire extinguishers in the lab to put it out. Your instructor will demonstrate the use of the fire extinguishers.
5. In case of a *large fire* involving the lab itself, evacuate the room and building according to the following procedure:
    a. Turn off all gas burners, and unplug electrical equipment.
    b. Leave the room and proceed to _____ _____.
    c. It is imperative that you assemble in front of the building so that your instructor can take roll to determine whether anyone is still inside. Do not wander off.

Accidents and First Aid

1. Report all accidents immediately. Your instructor will administer first aid as required.
2. For spills in or near the eyes, use the eyewash immediately.
3. For large spills on your body, use the safety shower.
4. For heat burns, chill the affected part with ice as soon as possible. Call your instructor.
5. Place a bandage on any cut or abrasion.

Power Outage

If the electricity goes off, be sure to turn off your gas jet. When the power is restored, the gas will come back on.

Earthquake

Turn off your gas jet and get under your lab desk during an earthquake. Your instructor will give any necessary evacuation instructions.

Orientation Walkabout

Locate the following items in the lab:

Broom and dustpan	Instructor's desk
Eyewash	Reference books
Fire blanket	Safety shower
Fire extinguisher	To Be Autoclaved area
First-aid cabinet	Biohazard containers
Fume hood	

Special Practices

1. Keep laboratory doors closed when experiments are in progress.
2. The instructor controls access to the laboratory and allows access only to people whose presence is required for program or support purposes.
3. Place contaminated materials that are to be decontaminated at a site away from the laboratory into a durable, leakproof container that is closed before being removed from the laboratory.
4. An insect and rodent control program is in effect.
5. A needle should not be bent, replaced in the sheath, or removed from the syringe following use. Place the needle and syringe promptly in a puncture-resistant container and decontaminate, preferably by autoclaving, before discarding them.
6. Inform your instructor if you are pregnant, are taking immunosuppressive drugs, or have any other medical condition (e.g., diabetes, immune deficiency) that might necessitate special precautions in the laboratory.
7. Potential pathogens used in the exercises in this manual are classified in Class 1 by the U.S. Public Health Service. These bacteria present a minimal hazard and require ordinary aseptic handling conditions (Biosafety Level 1). No special competence or containment is required. These organisms are the following:

   Enterobacter species
   Mycobacterium species
   Proteus species
   Pseudomonas aeruginosa
   Salmonella enterica Typhimurium
   Serratia marcescens
   Staphylococcus species
   Streptococcus species

Laboratory Facilities

1. Interior surfaces of walls, floors, and ceilings are water resistant so that they can be easily cleaned.
2. Benchtops are impervious to water and resistant to acids, alkalis, organic solvents, and moderate heat.
3. Windows in the laboratory are closed and sealed.

4. An autoclave for decontaminating laboratory wastes is available, preferably within the laboratory.

Contact with Blood and Other Body Fluids

The following procedures should be used by all health care workers, including students, whose activities involve contact with patients or with blood or other body fluids. While these procedures were developed by the CDC* to minimize the risk of transmitting HIV in a health care environment, adherence to these guidelines will minimize transmission of *all* infections.

1. Wear gloves for touching blood and body fluids, mucous membranes, or nonintact skin and for handling items or surfaces soiled with blood or body fluids. Change gloves after contact with each patient.
2. Wash hands and other skin surfaces immediately and thoroughly if they are contaminated with blood or other body fluids.
3. Wear masks and protective eyewear or face shields during procedures that are likely to generate droplets of blood or other body fluids.
4. Wear gowns or aprons during procedures that are likely to generate splashes of blood or other body fluids.
5. Wash hands and other skin surfaces immediately after gloves are removed.
6. Mouthpieces, resuscitation bags, or other ventilation devices should be available for use in areas in which the need for resuscitation is predictable. Emergency mouth-to-mouth resuscitation should be minimized.
7. Health care workers who have exudative lesions or weeping dermatitis should refrain from all direct patient care and from handling patient care equipment.
8. Pregnant health care workers are not known to be at greater risk of contracting HIV infection than health care workers who are not pregnant; however, if a health care worker develops HIV infection during pregnancy, the infant is at risk of infection. Because of this risk, pregnant health care workers should be especially familiar with and strictly adhere to precautions to minimize the risk of HIV transmission.
9. In a laboratory exercise where human blood is used, students should wear gloves or work only with their own blood and should dispose of all slides and blood-contaminated materials immediately after use. Any cuts or scrapes on the skin should be covered with a sterile bandage.

---

*CDC. "Recommendations for Prevention of HIV Transmission in Health-Care Settings." MMWR 38(S2), 1989.

General Safety in the Laboratory

During your microbiology course, you will learn how to safely handle fluids containing microorganisms. Through practice you will be able to perform experiments so that bacteria, fungai, and viruses remain in the desired containers, uncontaminated by microbes in the environment. These techniques, called **aseptic techniques,** will be a vital part of your work if you are going into health care or biotechnology.

1. Do not eat, drink, smoke, store food, or apply cosmetics in the laboratory.
2. Wear shoes at all times in the laboratory.
3. Tie back long hair.
4. Disinfect work surfaces at the beginning and end of every lab period and after every spill. The disinfectant used in this laboratory is _____.
5. Wash your hands before and after every laboratory period. Because bar soaps may become contaminated, use liquid or powdered soaps.
6. Use mechanical pipetting devices; do not use mouth pipetting.
7. Place a disinfectant-soaked paper towel on the desk while pipetting.
8. Wash your hands immediately and thoroughly if they become contaminated with microorganisms.
9. Cover spilled microbial cultures with paper towels, and saturate the towels with disinfectant. Leave covered for 20 minutes, and then clean up the spill and dispose of the towels.
10. Do not touch broken glassware with your hands; use a broom and dustpan. Place broken glassware contaminated with microbial cultures or body fluids in the To Be Autoclaved container. (See p. xii for what to do with broken glassware that is not contaminated.)
11. Place glassware and slides contaminated with blood, urine, and other body fluids in disinfectant.
12. Work only with your own body fluids and wastes in exercises requiring saliva, urine, blood, or feces, to prevent transmission of disease. The Centers for Disease Control and Prevention (CDC) state that "epidemiologic evidence has implicated only blood, semen, vaginal secretions, and breast milk in transmission of HIV." *Biosafety in Microbiological and Biomedical Laboratories,* www.cdc.gov.
13. Don't perform unauthorized experiments.
14. Don't use equipment without instruction.
15. Don't engage in horseplay in the laboratory.
16. If you got this far in the instructions, you'll probably do well in lab. Enjoy lab and make a new friend.

Procedures marked with this biohazard icon should be performed carefully to minimize the risk of transmitting disease.

I have read the above laboratory safety rules and agree to abide by them when in the laboratory.

Name: _____ Date: _____

Use and Care
of the Microscope

*The most important discoveries of the laws, methods and progress of nature
have nearly always sprung from the examination of the smallest objects which
she contains.*

JEAN BAPTISTE LAMARCK

Objectives

After completing this exercise, you should be able to:

1. Demonstrate the correct use of a compound light microscope.
2. Diagram the path of light through a compound microscope.
3. Name the major parts of a compound microscope.
4. Identify the three basic morphologies of bacteria.

Background

Virtually all organisms studied in microbiology cannot be seen with the naked eye but require the use of optical systems for magnification. The microscope was invented shortly before 1600 by Zacharias Janssen of the Netherlands. The microscope was not used to examine microorganisms until the 1680s, when a clerk in a dry-goods store, Antoni van Leeuwenhoek, examined scrapings of his teeth and any other substances he could find. The early microscopes, called **simple microscopes,** consisted of biconvex lenses and were essentially magnifying glasses. To see microbes, a compound microscope, which has two lenses between the eye and the object, is required. This optical system magnifies the object, and an illumination system (sun and mirror or lamp) ensures that adequate light is available for viewing. A **brightfield compound microscope,** which shows dark objects in a bright field, is used most often.

You will be using a brightfield compound microscope similar to the one shown in Figure 1a. The basic frame of the microscope consists of a **base,** a **stage** to hold the slide, an **arm** for carrying the microscope, and a **body tube** for transmitting the magnified image. The stage may have two clips or a movable mechanical stage to hold the slide. The light source is in the base. Above the light source is a **condenser,** which consists of several lenses that concentrate light on the slide by focusing it into a cone, as shown in Figure 1b. The condenser

has an **iris diaphragm,** which controls the angle and size of the cone of light. This ability to control the *amount* of light ensures that optimal light will reach the slide. Above the stage, on one end of the body tube, is a revolving nosepiece holding three or four **objective lenses.** At the upper end of the tube is an **ocular** or **eyepiece lens** ($10\times$ to $12.5\times$). If a microscope has only one ocular lens, it is called a **monocular** microscope; a **binocular** microscope has two ocular lenses.

By moving the tube closer to the slide or the stage closer to the objective lens, using the coarse- or fine-adjustment knobs, one can focus the image. The larger knob, the **coarse adjustment,** is used for focusing with the low-power objectives ($4\times$ and $10\times$), and the smaller knob, the **fine adjustment,** is used for focusing with the high-power and oil immersion lenses. The coarse-adjustment knob moves the lenses or the stage longer distances. The area seen through a microscope is called the **field of vision.**

The **magnification** of a microscope depends on the type of objective lens used with the ocular. Compound microscopes have three or four objective lenses mounted on a nosepiece: scanning ($4\times$), low-power ($10\times$), high-dry ($40\times$ to $45\times$), and oil immersion ($97\times$ to $100\times$). The magnification provided by each lens is stamped on the barrel. The total magnification of the object is calculated by multiplying the magnification of the ocular (usually $10\times$) by the magnification of the objective lens. The most important lens in microbiology is the **oil immersion lens;** it has the highest magnification ($97\times$ to $100\times$) and must be used with immersion oil. Optical systems could be built to magnify much more than the $1000\times$ magnification of your microscope, but the resolution would be poor.

Resolution or **resolving power** refers to the ability of lenses to reveal fine detail or two points distinctly separated. An example of resolution involves a car approaching you at night. At first only one light appears, but as the car nears, you can distinguish two

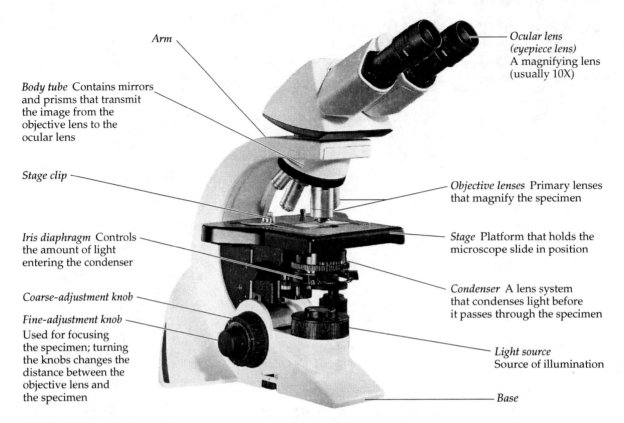

Arm

Ocular lens
(eyepiece lens)
A magnifying lens
(usually 10X)

Body tube Contains mirrors
and prisms that transmit
the image from the
objective lens to the
ocular lens

Stage clip

Objective lenses Primary lenses
that magnify the specimen

Iris diaphragm Controls
the amount of light
entering the condenser

Stage Platform that holds the
microscope slide in position

Coarse-adjustment knob

Condenser A lens system
that condenses light before
it passes through the specimen

Fine-adjustment knob
Used for focusing
the specimen; turning
the knobs changes the
distance between the
objective lens and
the specimen

Light source
Source of illumination

Base

(a) Principal parts and functions

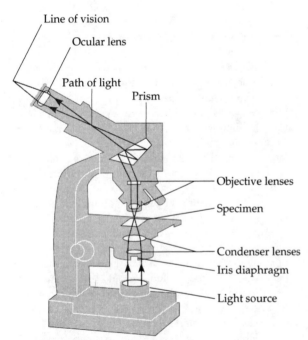

Line of vision

Ocular lens

Path of light

Prism

Objective lenses

Specimen

Condenser lenses

Iris diaphragm

Light source

(b) Arrows show the path of light (bottom to top)

Figure 1

The compound light microscope. (a) Its principal parts and
their functions. (b) Lines from the light source through the
ocular lens illustrate the path of light.

headlights. The resolving power is a function of the wavelength of light used and a characteristic of the lens system called **numerical aperture.** Resolving power is best when two objects are seen as distinct even though they are very close together. Resolving power is expressed in units of length; the smaller the distance, the better the resolving power.

$$\text{Resolving power} = \frac{\text{Wavelength of light used}}{2 \times \text{numerical aperture}}$$

Smaller wavelengths of light improve resolving power. The effect of decreasing the wavelength can be seen in electron microscopes, which use electrons as a source of "light." The electrons have an extremely short wavelength and result in excellent resolving power. A light microscope has a resolving power of about 200 nanometers (nm), whereas an electron microscope has a resolving power of less than 0.2 nm. The numerical aperture is engraved on the side of each objective lens (usually abbreviated N.A.). If the numerical aperture increases—for example, from 0.65 to 1.25—the resolving power is improved. The numerical aperture is dependent on the maximum angle of the light entering the objective lens and on the **refractive index** (the amount the light bends) of the material (usually air) between the objective lens and the slide. This relationship is defined by the following:

N.A. = $N \sin \theta$
    N = Refractive index of medium
    θ = Angle between the most divergent light ray
             gathered by the lens and the center of the lens

As shown in Figure 2, light is refracted when it emerges from the slide because of the change in media as the light passes from glass to air. When immersion oil is placed between the slide and the oil immersion lens, the light ray continues without refraction because immersion oil has the same refractive index ($N = 1.52$) as glass ($N = 1.52$). This can be seen easily. When you look through a bottle of immersion oil, you cannot see the glass rod in it because of the identical N values of the glass and immersion oil. The result of using oil is that light loss is minimized, and the lens focuses very close to the slide.

As light rays pass through a lens, they are bent to converge at the **focal point,** where an image is formed (Figure 3a). When you bring the center of a microscope field into focus, the periphery may be fuzzy due to the curvature of the lens, resulting in multiple focal points. This is called **spherical aberration** (Figure 3b). Spherical aberrations can be minimized by the use of the iris diaphragm, which eliminates light rays to the periphery of the lens, or by a series of lenses resulting in essentially a flat optical system. Sometimes a multitude of colors, or **chromatic aberration,** is seen in the

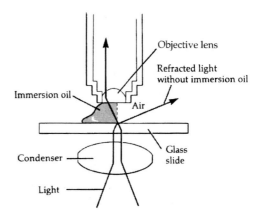

Figure 2

Refractive index. Because the refractive indexes of the glass microscope slide and immersion oil are the same, the oil keeps the light rays from refracting.

field (Figure 3c). This is caused by the prismlike effect of the lens as various wavelengths of white light pass through to a different focal point for each wavelength. Chromatic aberrations can be minimized by the use of filters (usually blue); or by lens systems corrected for red and blue light, called *achromatic lenses;* or by lenses corrected for red, blue, and other wavelengths, called *apochromatic lenses.* The most logical, but most expensive, method of eliminating chromatic aberrations is to use a light source of one wavelength, or **monochromatic light.**

Compound microscopes require a light source. The light may be reflected to the condenser by a mirror under the stage. If your microscope has a mirror, the sun or a lamp may be used as the light source. Most compound microscopes have a built-in illuminator in the base. The *intensity* of the light can often be adjusted with a rheostat.

The microscope is a very important tool in microbiology, and it must be used carefully and correctly. Follow these guidelines *every* time you use a microscope.

General Guidelines

1. Carry the microscope with both hands: one hand beneath the base and one hand on the arm.
2. Do not tilt the microscope; instead, adjust your stool so you can comfortably use the instrument.
3. Observe the slide with both eyes open, to avoid eyestrain.
4. Always focus by moving the lens away from the slide.
5. Always focus slowly and carefully.

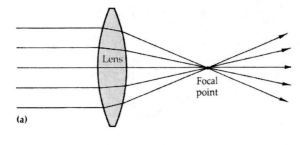

(a)

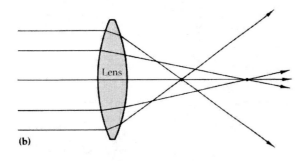

(b)

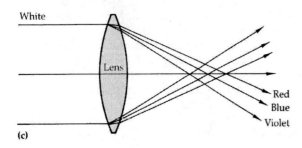

(c)

Figure 3

Focal point. **(a)** An image is formed when light converges at one point, called the focal point. **(b)** Spherical aberration. Curved lenses result in light passing through one region of the lens having a different focal point than light passing through another part of the lens. **(c)** Chromatic aberration. Each wavelength of light may be given a different focal point by the lens.

6. When using the low-power lens, the iris diaphragm should be barely open so that good contrast is achieved. More light is needed with higher magnification.

7. Before using the oil immersion lens, have your slide in focus under high power. *Always focus with low power first.*

8. Keep the stage clean and free of oil. Keep all lenses except the oil immersion lens free of oil.

9. Keep all lenses clean. Use *only* lens paper to clean them. Wipe oil off the oil immersion lens before putting your microscope away. Do not touch the lenses with your hands.

10. Clean the ocular lens carefully with lens paper. If dust is present, it will rotate as you turn the lens.

11. After use, remove the slide, wipe oil off it, put the dust cover on the microscope, and return it to the designated area.

12. When a problem does arise with the microscope, obtain help from the instructor. Do not use another microscope unless yours is declared "out of action."

Materials

Compound light microscope

Immersion oil

Lens paper

Prepared slides of algae, fungi, protozoa, and bacteria

Procedure

1. Place the microscope on the bench squarely in front of you.

2. Obtain a slide of algae or fungi and place it in the side clips on the stage.

3. Adjust the eyepieces on a binocular microscope to your own personal measurements.
   a. Look through the eyepieces and, using the thumb wheel, adjust the distance between the eyepieces until one circle of light appears.
   b. With the low-power (10×) objective in place, cover the left eyepiece with a small card and focus the microscope on the slide. When the right eyepiece has been focused, remove your hand from the focusing knobs and cover the right eyepiece. Looking through the microscope with your left eye, focus the left eyepiece by turning the eyepiece adjustment. Make a note of the number at which you focused the left eyepiece so you can adjust any binocular microscope for your eyes.

4. Raise the condenser up to the stage. On some microscopes, the condenser can be focused by the following procedure:
   a. Focus with the 10× objective.
   b. Close the iris diaphragm so only a minimum of light enters the objective lens.

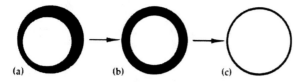

Figure 4

Using low power, lower the condenser until a distinct circle of light is visible (a). Center the circle of light using the centering screws (b). Open the iris diaphragm until the light just fills the field (c).

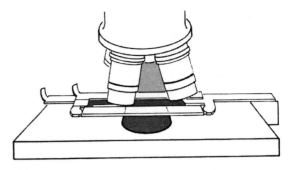

(a) Move the high-dry lens out of position.

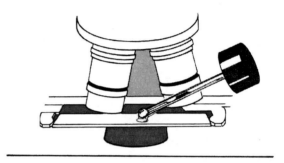

(b) Place a drop of immersion oil in the center of the slide.

c. Lower the condenser until the light is seen as a circle in the center of the field. On some microscopes the circle of light may be centered (Figure 4) using the centering screws found on the condenser.

d. Raise the condenser up to the slide, lower it, and stop when the color on the periphery changes from pink to blue (usually 1 or 2 mm below the stage).

e. Open the iris diaphragm until the light just fills the field.

5. Diagram some of the cells on the slide under low power. Use a minimum of light by adjusting the _____.

6. When an image has been brought into focus with low power, rotate the turret to the next lens, and the subject will remain almost in focus. All of the objectives (with the possible exception of the 4×) are **parfocal;** that is, when a subject is in focus with one lens, it will be in focus with all of the lenses. When you have completed your observations under low power, swing the high-dry objective into position and focus. Use the fine adjustment. Only a slight adjustment should be required. Why? _____

More light is usually needed. Again, draw the general size and shape of some cells.

7. Move the high-dry lens out of position, and place a drop of immersion oil on the area of the slide you are observing. Carefully click the oil immersion lens into position. It should now be immersed in the oil (Figure 5). Careful use of the fine-adjustment knob should bring the object into focus. Note the shape and size of the cells. Did the color of the

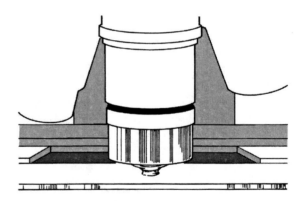

(c) Move the oil immersion lens into position.

Figure 5

Using the oil immersion lens.

cells change with the different lenses? _____
Did the size of the field change? _____

8. Record your observations and note the magnifications.

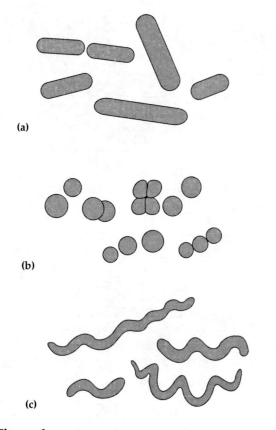

(a)

(b)

(c)

Figure 6

Basic shapes of bacteria. **(a)** Bacillus (plural: bacilli), or rod.
(b) Coccus (plural: cocci). **(c)** Spiral.

9. When your observations are completed, move the turret to bring a low-power objective into position. *Do not* rotate the high-dry (40×) objective through the immersion oil. Clean the oil off the objective lens with lens paper, and clean off the slide with tissue paper or a paper towel. Remove the slide. Repeat this procedure with all the available slides. When observing the bacteria, note the three different morphologies, or shapes, shown in Figure 6.

Use and Care of the Microscope

NAME _____

DATE _____

LAB SECTION _____

Purpose _____

_____

_____

Data

Microscope number: _____ Monocular or binocular: _____

Eyepiece adjustment notes: _____

Draw a few representative cells from each slide and show how they appeared at each magnification. Note the differences in size at each magnification.

Algae

Slide of _____

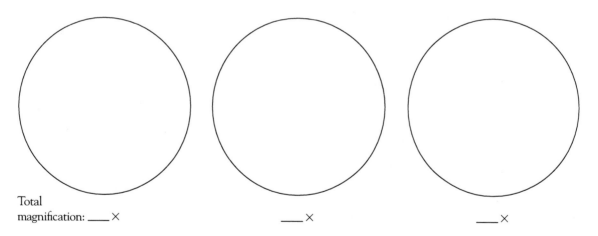

Total
magnification: ___ ×   ___ ×   ___ ×

Fungi

Slide of _____

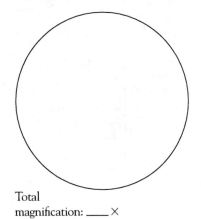 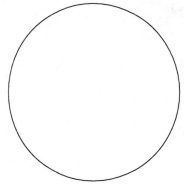 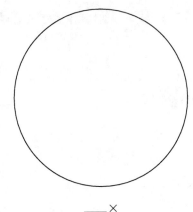

Total
magnification: ___ ×   ___ ×   ___ ×

Protozoa

Slide of _____

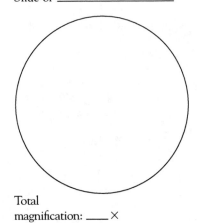 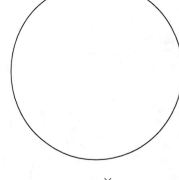 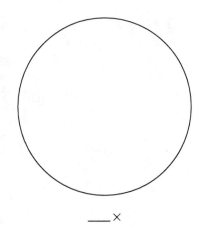

Total
magnification: ___ ×   ___ ×   ___ ×

Bacteria

Slide of _____

Be sure to sketch all bacterial shapes observed.

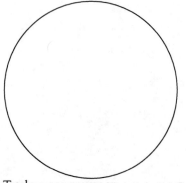 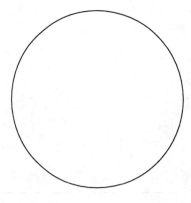 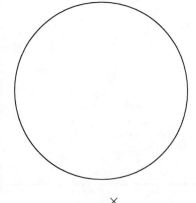

Total
magnification: ___ ×   ___ ×   ___ ×

Questions

1. Why is it desirable that microscope objectives be parfocal? _____

    _____

    _____

2. Which objective focuses closest to the slide? _____

    _____

    _____

3. What controls the amount of light reaching the ocular lens? _____

    _____

    _____

4. Is your lens corrected for chromatic aberrations? _____

5. What three bacterial shapes did you observe? _____

    _____

Critical Thinking

1. Assume the diameter of the field of vision in your microscope is 2 mm under low power. If one *Bacillus* cell is 2 μm, how many *Bacillus* cells could fit end to end across the field? How many 10 μm yeast cells could fit across the field?

2. What effect does increased magnification have on the field of vision?

3. Name two ways in which you can enhance the resolving power.

4. What advantages does the low-power objective have over the oil immersion objective for viewing fungi?

5. What would occur if water were accidentally used in place of immersion oil?

Examination of Living Microorganisms

Objectives

After completing this exercise, you should be able to:

1. Prepare and observe wet-mount slides and hanging-drop slides.
2. Distinguish between true motility and Brownian movement.
3. Use a phase-contrast microscope.
4. Explain how phase-contrast and darkfield microscopy differ from brightfield microscopy.

Background

Antoni van Leeuwenhoek was the first known individual to observe living microbes in a suspension. Unfortunately, he was very protective of his homemade microscopes and left no descriptions of how to make them. During his lifetime he kept "for himself alone" his microscopes and his method of observing "animalcules." Directions for making a replica of van Leeuwenhoek's microscope can be found in *American Biology Teacher*.* Fortunately, you will not have to make your own microscope.

In **brightfield microscopy,** objects are dark and the field is light. Brightfield microscopy can be used to observe unstained microorganisms. However, because the optical properties of the organisms and their aqueous environment are similar, very little contrast can be seen. Two other types of compound microscopes, however, are useful for observing living organisms: darkfield and phase-contrast microscopes. These microscopes optically increase contrasts between the organism and background by using special condensers.

In **darkfield microscopy,** the objects are light and the field is dark. In brightfield microscopy, light rays that strike the specimen are reflected away from the lens (Figure 1a). The darkfield condenser concentrates the light into a hollow cone of light at such an angle that none of the light rays reach the objective lens unless they pass through an object such as a cell to change their direction (Figure 1b). An opaque darkfield disk eliminates all central light rays. Thus, the objects

appear brightly illuminated against a dark background. Darkfield microscopy allows the investigator to observe the shape and motility of unstained live organisms. Darkfield microscopy is valuable for observing the spirochete (*Treponema pallidum*) that causes syphilis. This bacterium is not stainable with conventional stains but can be observed in direct smears with darkfield microscopy.

In **phase-contrast microscopy,** small differences in the refractive properties of the objects and the aqueous environment are transformed into corresponding variations of brightness. In phase-contrast microscopy, a ring of light passes through the object, and light rays are **diffracted** (retarded) and out of phase with the light rays not hitting the object. The phase-contrast microscope enhances these phase differences so that the eye detects the difference as contrast (Figure 2) between the organisms and background and between structures within a cell. In phase-contrast microscopy, the organisms appear as degrees of brightness against a darker background. The advantage of phase-contrast microscopy is that structural detail within live cells can be studied.

In this exercise, you will examine, using wet-mount techniques, different environments to help you become aware of the numbers and varieties of microbes found in nature. The microbes will exhibit either Brownian movement or true motility. **Brownian movement** is not true motility but rather movement caused by the molecules in the liquid striking an object and causing the object to shake or bounce. In Brownian movement, the particles and microorganisms all vibrate at about the same rate and maintain their relative positions. Motile microorganisms move from one position to another. Their movement appears more directed than Brownian movement, and occasionally the cells may spin or roll.

Many kinds of microbes, such as protozoa, algae, fungi, and bacteria, can be found in pond water and in infusions of organic matter. Van Leeuwenhoek made some of his discoveries using a peppercorn infusion similar to the one you will see in this exercise. Direct examination of living microorganisms is very useful in determining size, shape, and movement. A wet mount is a fast way to observe bacteria. Motility and larger

---

*W. G. Walter and H. Via. "Making a Leeuwenhoek Microscope Replica." *American Biology Teacher* 30(6):537–539, 1968.

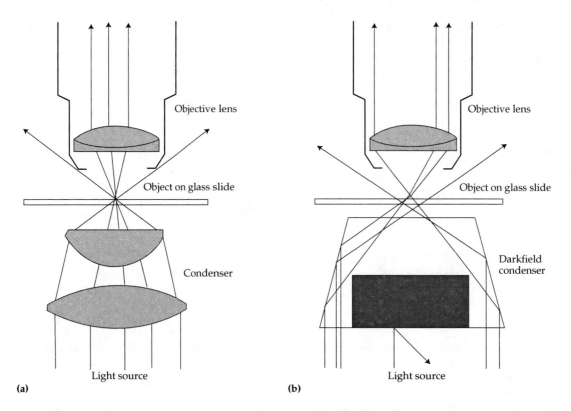

Figure 1

A comparison of brightfield and darkfield microscopy. (**a**) In brightfield microscopy, light is reflected away from the objective lens by the specimen. (**b**) In darkfield microscopy, only light rays that go through the object reach the objective lens.

microbes are more easily observed in the greater depth provided by a hanging drop. Evaporation of the suspended drop of fluid is reduced by using a petroleum jelly seal.

In this exercise, you will examine living microorganisms by brightfield and by phase-contrast microscopy.

Materials

Slides

Coverslips

Hanging-drop (depression) slide

Petroleum jelly

Toothpick

Pasteur pipettes

Alcohol

Gram's iodine

Phase-contrast microscope and centering telescope

Inoculating loop

Cultures

Hay infusion, incubated 1 week in light

Hay infusion, incubated 1 week in dark

Peppercorn infusion

Pond water with algae

18- to 24-hour-old broth culture of *Bacillus*

Techniques Required

Compound light microscopy

Procedure

Wet-Mount Technique

1. Suspend the infusions by stirring or shaking them carefully. Using a Pasteur pipette, transfer a small drop of one hay infusion to a slide or transfer a loopful using the inoculating loop, as demonstrated by your instructor.
2. Handle the coverslip carefully by its edges and place it on the drop.

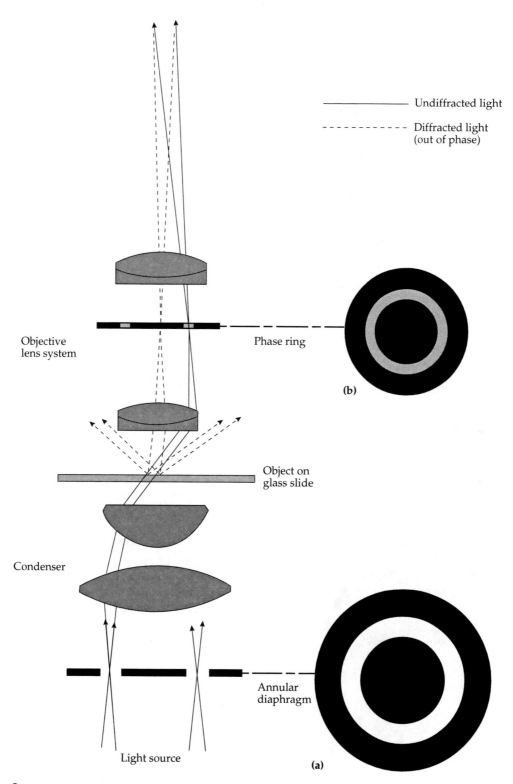

Undiffracted light

Diffracted light
(out of phase)

Objective
lens system

Phase ring

(b)

Object on
glass slide

Condenser

Annular
diaphragm

Light source

(a)

Figure 2

Phase-contrast microscopy. **(a)** A hollow cone of light is formed by the annular
diaphragm. Diffracted rays are further retarded by the phase ring **(b)** in the
objective lens.

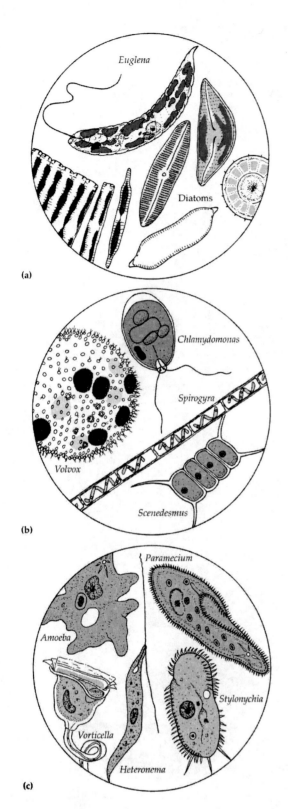

(a)

(b)

(c)

Figure 3

Some common protozoa and algae that can be found in infusions: (**a** and **b**) algae and (**c**) protozoa.

3. Gently press on the coverslip with the end of a pencil or loop handle.
4. Place the slide on the microscope stage and observe it with low power (10×). Adjust the iris diaphragm so a small amount of light is admitted. Concentrate your observations on the larger, more rapidly moving organisms. At this magnification, bacteria are barely discernible as tiny dots. Figure 3 and Color Plate XIII may help you to identify some of the microorganisms.
5. Examine the slide with the high-dry lens (40×); then increase the light and focus carefully. Bacteria should now be magnified sufficiently to be seen.
6. After recording your observations, examine the slide with the oil immersion lens. Some microorganisms are motile, while others exhibit Brownian movement.
7. If you want to observe the motile organisms further, place a drop of alcohol or Gram's iodine at the edge of the coverslip and allow it to run under and mix with the infusion. What does the alcohol or iodine do to these organisms? _____

_____
They can now be observed more carefully.
8. Record your observations, noting the relative size and shape of the organisms.
9. Make a wet mount from the other hay infusion, and observe it, using the low and high-dry objectives. Record your observations.
10. Clean all the slides and return them to the slide box. Coverslips can be discarded in the disinfectant jar. Wipe the oil from the objective lens with lens paper.

Hanging-Drop Procedure

1. Obtain a clean hanging-drop (depression) slide.
2. Pick up a small amount of petroleum jelly on a toothpick.
3. Pick up a coverslip (by its edges) and carefully touch the petroleum jelly with an edge of the coverslip to get a small rim of petroleum jelly. Repeat with the other three edges (Figure 4a), keeping the petroleum jelly on the same side of the coverslip.
4. Place the coverslip on a paper towel, with the petroleum jelly-side up.
5. Transfer a small drop or loopful of the peppercorn infusion to the coverslip (Figure 4b).
6. Place a depression slide over the drop and quickly invert it so the drop is suspended (Figure 4c). Why should the drop be hanging? _____

_____
7. Examine the drop under low power (Figure 4d) by locating the edge of the drop and moving the slide so the edge of the drop crosses the center of the field.

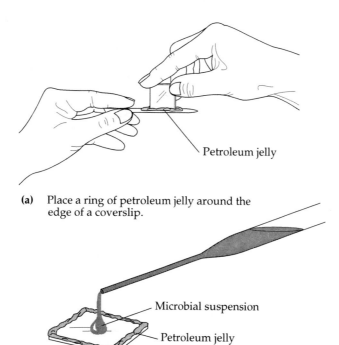

(a) Place a ring of petroleum jelly around the edge of a coverslip.

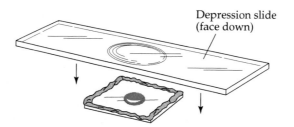

Microbial suspension

Petroleum jelly

(b) Place a drop of an infusion in the center of the coverslip.

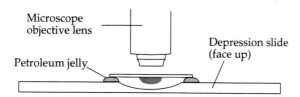

Depression slide (face down)

(c) Place the depression slide on the coverslip.

Microscope objective lens

Petroleum jelly

Depression slide (face up)

(d) Turn the slide over; place the slide, coverslip up, on the microscope stage; and observe it under the low and high-dry objectives.

Figure 4

Hanging-drop preparation.

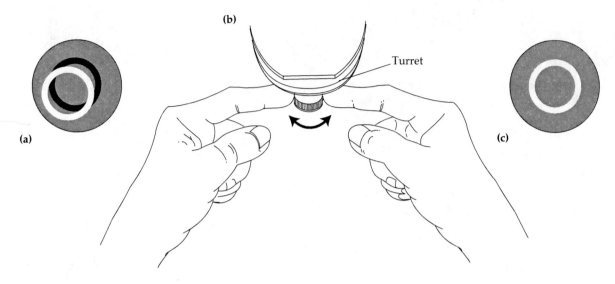

(b)

Turret

(a)

(c)

Figure 5

Adjustment of phase rings. **(a)** The two images seen before adjustment of the phase rings. By moving the wheel under the condenser turret **(b)**, the images are made to coincide **(c)**.

8. Reduce the light with the iris diaphragm and focus. Observe the different sizes, shapes, and types of movement.
9. Switch to high-dry and record your observations. Do not focus down. Why not? _____

_____

Do not attempt to use the oil immersion lens.
10. When finished, clean your slide and, using a new coverslip, repeat the procedure with the culture of *Bacillus*. Record your observations.
11. Return your microscope to its proper location. Clean your slides well and return them. Discard the coverslips in the disinfectant jar.

Phase-Contrast Microscopy

1. Make a wet mount of any of the suspensions.
2. Place the slide on the stage and turn on the light.
3. Start with the 10× objective and move the condenser diaphragm to match setting "10."
4. Focus on an obvious clump of material with the coarse and fine adjustments.
5. Close the iris diaphragm, and move the condenser up and down until a light octagon comes into focus. Then open the diaphragm until light just fills the field.
6. Adjust the phase rings.
   a. Replace the eyepiece (screw out) with the centering telescope, and focus the telescope on the phase plate ring by revolving its head.

   b. You will see two rings (Figure 5a): one, a bright image of the phase ring, and the other, the dark image of the phase plate in the objective. Adjust the knurled wheel under the condenser turret with your fingertips (Figure 5b) to make the bright image coincide with the dark ring (Figure 5c). Do not touch the iris diaphragm.
   c. When the ring has been centered (Figure 5c), replace the telescope with the ocular lens.
7. Observe.
8. Focus the slide with the 40× objective and the 40× condenser turret.
9. Readjust the phase rings using the telescope, as done in step 6. Record your observations. Can you distinguish any of the organelles in the organisms?

10. Focus the slide with the 100× objective and the 100× condenser turret, and then readjust the phase rings using the telescope. Diagram your observations.
11. Clean the slide. Make a wet mount of one other sample. Observe. Are motile organisms present?

_____

Compare your observations with those made with the brightfield microscope.

Examination of Living Microorganisms

NAME _____

DATE _____

LAB SECTION _____

Purpose _____

_____

_____

Data

Wet-Mount Technique

Draw the types of protozoa, algae, fungi, and bacteria observed. Indicate their relative sizes and shapes. Record the magnification.

Sample: Hay infusion, light   Hay infusion, dark

Total
magnification: ___ ×   ___ ×

Compare the size and shape of organisms observed in the "light" and "dark" hay infusion.

_____

_____

_____

Hanging-Drop Procedure

Draw the types of microorganisms seen under high-dry magnification. Indicate their relative sizes and shapes.

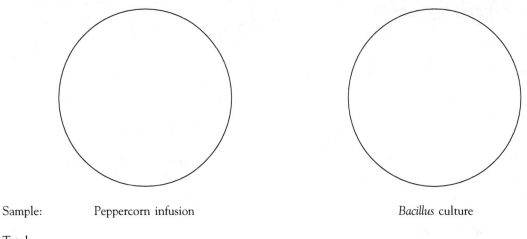

Sample: Peppercorn infusion   *Bacillus* culture

Total
magnification: ___×   ___×

Phase-Contrast Microscopy

Carefully draw the organisms and their internal structure.

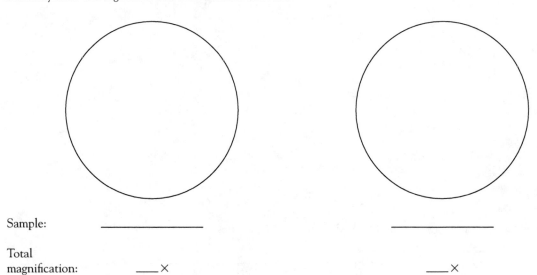

Sample: _____   _____

Total
magnification: ___×   ___×

Bacteria

In the following table, record the relative numbers of each bacterial shape observed. Record your data as 4+ (most abundant), 3+, 2+, +, − (not seen).

Culture	Shape		
	Bacilli (rods)	Cocci	Spiral
Hay infusion, dark			
Hay infusion, light			
Peppercorn infusion			
Bacillus culture			
Pond water			

Questions

1. What, if any, practical value do these techniques have? _____

   _____

2. Did any of the bacteria exhibit true motility? _____ How do you distinguish true motility from Brownian

   movement or motion of the fluid? _____

   _____

3. What is the advantage of the hanging-drop procedure over the wet mount? _____

   _____

4. Compare the appearance of microorganisms observed using phase-contrast microscopy versus brightfield

   microscopy. _____

   _____

   _____

5. Why is petroleum jelly used in the hanging-drop procedure? _____

   _____

   _____

6. Which infusion had the most bacteria? _____ Briefly explain why. _____

_____

_____

_____

Critical Thinking

1. Why are microorganisms hard to see in wet preparations?

2. Can you distinguish the prokaryotic organisms from the eukaryotic organisms? Explain.

3. Why isn't the oil immersion lens used in the hanging-drop procedure?

4. From where did the organisms in the infusions come?

Preparation of Smears and Simple Staining

Objectives

After completing this exercise, you should be able to:

1. Prepare and fix a smear.
2. List the advantages of staining microorganisms.
3. Explain the basic mechanism of staining.
4. Perform a simple direct stain.

Background

Most stains used in microbiology are synthetic aniline (coal tar derivative) dyes derived from benzene. The dyes are usually salts, although a few are acids or bases, composed of charged colored ions. The ion that is colored is referred to as a **chromophore.** For example,

$$\text{Methylene blue chloride} \leftrightarrows \text{Methylene blue}^+ + \text{Cl}^-$$
$$\text{(Chromophore)}$$

If the chromophore is a positive ion like the methylene blue in the equation shown, the stain is considered a **basic stain;** if it is a negative ion, it is an **acidic stain.** Most bacteria are stained when a basic stain permeates the cell wall and adheres by weak ionic bonds to the negative charges of the bacterial cell.

Staining procedures that use only one stain are called **simple stains.** A simple stain that stains the bacteria is a **direct stain,** and a simple stain that stains the background but leaves the bacteria unstained is a **negative stain.** Simple stains can be used to determine cell morphology, size, and arrangement.

Before bacteria can be stained, a thin film of bacterial cells, called a **smear,** must be placed on a slide. A smear is made by spreading a bacterial suspension on a clean slide and allowing it to air-dry. The smear must be **fixed** to kill the bacteria; coagulated proteins from the cells will cause cells to stick to the slide. The dry smear is passed through a Bunsen burner flame several times to **heat-fix** the bacteria. Heat fixing may not kill all the bacteria. Alternatively, the dry smear can be placed on a 60°C slide warmer for 10 minutes or until chemically fixed. To **chemically fix** the bacteria, cover the smear with 95% methyl alcohol for 1 minute. Fixing denatures bacterial enzymes, preventing them from digesting cell parts, which causes the cell to break, a process called *autolysis*. Fixing also enhances the adherence of bacterial cells to the microscope slide.

Materials

Methylene blue

Wash bottle of distilled water

Slide

Inoculating loop

Cultures

Staphylococcus epidermidis slant

Bacillus megaterium broth

Techniques Required

Compound light microscopy

Inoculating loop

Procedure

1. Clean your slide well with abrasive soap or cleanser; rinse and dry. Handle clean slides by the end or edge. Use a marker to make two dime-sized circles on the bottom of each slide so they will not wash off. Label each circle according to the bacterial culture used.
2. Sterilize your inoculating loop by holding it in the hottest part of the flame (at the edge of the inner blue area) or the electric incinerator until it is red-hot. The entire wire should get red. Allow the loop to cool so that bacteria picked up with the loop won't be killed. Allow the loop to cool without touching it or setting it down. Cooling takes about 30 seconds. You will determine the appropriate time with a little practice.

 The loop must be cool before inserting it into a medium. A hot loop will spatter the medium and move bacteria into the air.

Preparation of Smears and Simple Staining

(a) Mark the smear areas with a marking pencil on the underside of a clean slide.

FROM SOLID MEDIUM

FROM LIQUID MEDIUM

(b) Place 1 or 2 loopfuls of water on the slide.

(d) Place 2 or 3 loopfuls of the liquid culture on the slide with a sterile loop.

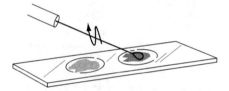

(c) Transfer a very small amount of the culture with a sterile loop. Mix with the water on the slide.

(e) Spread the bacteria within the circle.

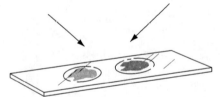

(f) Allow the smears to air-dry at room temperature.

or

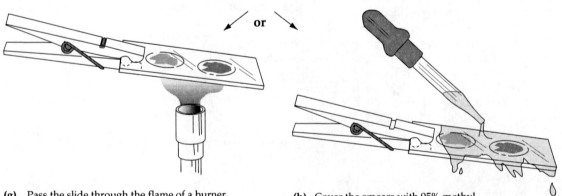

(g) Pass the slide through the flame of a burner two or three times.

(h) Cover the smears with 95% methyl alcohol for 1 minute, and then let the smears air-dry.

Figure 1

Preparing a bacterial smear.

3. Prepare smears (Figure 1).
   a. Make a smear of bacteria from the broth culture in the center of one circle. Flick the tube of broth culture lightly with your finger to resuspend sedimented bacteria, and place 2 or 3 loopfuls of the culture in the circle. Sterilize your loop between each loopful. Spread the culture within the circle.
   b. Sterilize your loop.

 Always sterilize your loop after using it and before setting it down.

   c. For the bacterial culture on solid media, place 1 or 2 loopfuls of distilled water in the center of the other circle, using the sterile inoculating loop. Which bacterium is on a solid medium? _____
   Sterilize your loop.
   d. Using the cooled loop, scrape a *small* amount of the culture off the slant—do not take the agar (Figure 2). If you hear the sizzle of boiling water when you touch the agar with the loop, resterilize your loop and begin again. Why? _____
   Try not to gouge the agar. Emulsify (to a milky suspension) the cells in the drop of water, and spread the suspension to fill a majority of the circle. The smear should look like diluted skim milk. Sterilize your loop again.
   e. Let the smears dry. *Do not* blow on the slide because this will move the bacterial suspension. *Do not* flame the slide because flaming will distort the cells' shapes.
   f. Hold the slide with a clothespin and fix the smears by one of the following methods (Figure 1g or h):
   (1) Pass the slide quickly through the blue flame two or three times or place it on a 60° slide warmer for 10 minutes.
   (2) Cover the smear with 95% methyl alcohol for 1 minute. Tip the slide to let the alcohol run off, and let the slide air-dry before staining. Do not fix until the smears are completely dry. Why? _____
   _____

5. Stain smears (Figure 3).
   a. Use a clothespin to hold the slide, or place it on a staining rack.
   b. Cover the smear with methylene blue and leave it for 30 to 60 seconds (Figure 3a).

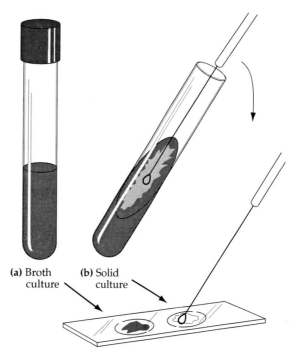

(a) Broth culture   (b) Solid culture

Figure 2

Transferring bacteria. (a) Transfer 2 or 3 loopfuls of microbial suspension to a slide. (b) Gently scrape bacteria from the agar surface and transfer the bacteria to a loopful of water on a slide. Be careful to avoid gouging into the agar.

   c. Carefully wash the excess stain off with distilled water from a wash bottle. Let the water run down the tilted slide (Figure 3b).
   d. Gently blot the smear with a paper towel or absorbent paper and let it dry (Figure 3c).
6. Examine your stained smears microscopically using the low, high-dry, and oil immersion objectives. Put the oil *directly* on the smear; coverslips are not needed. Record your observations with labeled drawings.
7. Blot the oil from the objective lens with lens paper, and return your microscope to its proper location. Clean your slides well, or save them as described in step 8.
8. Stained bacterial slides can be stored in a slide box. Remove the oil from the slide by blotting it with a paper towel. Any residual oil won't matter.

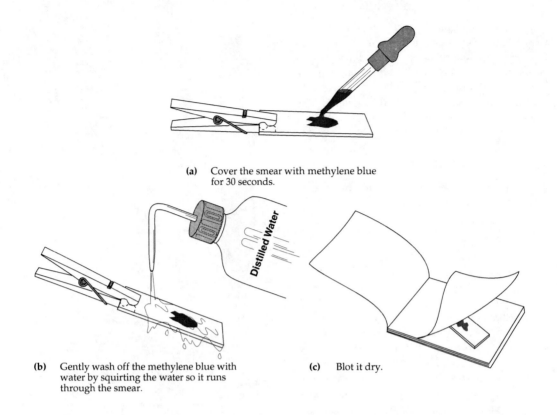

(a) Cover the smear with methylene blue for 30 seconds.

(b) Gently wash off the methylene blue with water by squirting the water so it runs through the smear.

(c) Blot it dry.

Figure 3

Simple staining.

LABORATORY REPORT

Preparation of Smears and Simple Staining

NAME _____

DATE _____

LAB SECTION_____

Purpose _____

_____

_____

Data

Sketch a few bacteria viewed with the oil immersion objective lens.

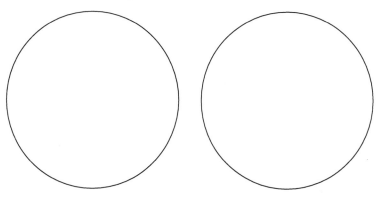

Bacteria:	*Staphylococcus epidermidis*	*Bacillus megaterium*
Total magnification:	___×	___×
Morphology (shape):	_____	_____
Arrangement of cells relative to one another:	_____	_____

Questions

1. Which bacterium is a rod? _____

2. Of what value is a simple stain? _____

_____

_____

3. What is the purpose of fixing the smear? _____

    _____

4. What are the two methods of fixing a smear? _____

    Which one did you use? _____

5. In heat fixing, what would happen if too much heat were applied? _____

    _____

Critical Thinking

1. Methylene blue can be prepared as a basic stain or an acidic stain. How would the pH of the stain affect the staining of bacteria?

2. Can dyes other than methylene blue be used for direct staining? Briefly explain.

3. Bacteria can be seen without staining. Why then was Koch's recommendation for fixing and staining important for microbiology?

Negative Staining

Objectives

After completing this exercise, you should be able to:

1. Explain the application and mechanism of the negative stain technique.
2. Prepare a negative stain.

Background

The **negative stain** technique does not stain the bacteria but stains the background. The bacteria will appear clear against a stained background. The stain does not stain the bacteria because of ionic repulsion: The bacteria and the acidic stain both have negative charges.

No heat fixing or strong chemicals are used so the bacteria are less distorted than in other staining procedures. The negative stain technique is useful in situations where other staining techniques don't clearly indicate cell morphology or size.

Materials

Nigrosin

Clean slides (6)

Distilled water

Sterile toothpicks

Cultures

Bacillus subtilis

Staphylococcus epidermidis

Techniques Required

Compound light microscopy

Smear preparation

Procedure (Figure 1)

1. Slides must be clean and grease-free.
2. a. Place a *small* drop of nigrosin at the end of the slide. For cultures on solid media, add a loopful of distilled water and emulsify a small amount of the culture in the nigrosin-water drop. For broth cultures, mix a loopful of the culture into the drop of nigrosin (Figure 1a). Do not spread the drop or let it dry.
   b. Using the end edge of another slide, spread out the drop (Figure 1b and c) to produce a smear varying from opaque black to gray. The angle of the spreading slide will determine the thickness of the smear.
   c. Let the smear air-dry (Figure 1d). *Do not heat-fix it.*
   d. Prepare a negative stain of the other culture.
3. Examine the stained slides microscopically, using the low, high-dry, and oil immersion objectives (Figure 2). As a general rule, if a few short rods are seen with small cocci, the morphology is rod shaped. The apparent cocci are short rods viewed from the end or products of the cell division of small rods.
4. a. Place a small drop of nigrosin and a loopful of water at the end of a slide.
   b. Scrape the base of your teeth and gums with a sterile toothpick.
   c. Mix the nigrosin-water with the toothpick to get an emulsion of bacteria from your mouth.

 Discard the toothpick in disinfectant.

   d. Follow steps 2b and 2c to complete the negative stain. Observe the stain and describe your results.

 Discard your slides in disinfectant.

5. Wipe the oil off your microscope and return it.

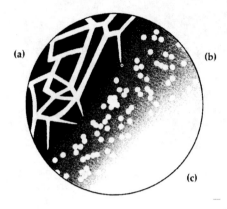

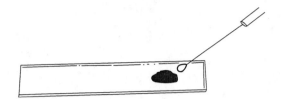

(a) Place a small drop of nigrosin near one end of a slide. Mix a loopful of broth culture in the drop. When the organisms are taken from a solid medium, mix a loopful of water in the nigrosin.

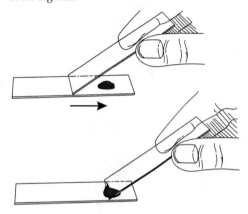

Figure 2

A negative stain viewed under a microscope. **(a)** This part of the smear is too heavy: Cracks in the stain can be seen. **(b)** Colorless cells are visible here. **(c)** Too little stain is in this area of the smear.

(b) Gently draw a second slide across the surface of the first until it contacts the drop. The drop will spread across the edge of the top slide.

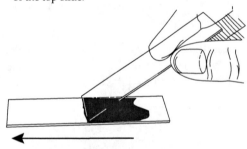

(c) Push the top slide to the left along the entire surface of the bottom slide.

(d) Let the smear air-dry.

Figure 1

Preparing a negative stain.

Negative Staining

NAME _____

DATE _____

LAB SECTION _____

Purpose _____

_____

_____

Data

Sketch a few bacteria (oil immersion objective lens).

Specimen: *Bacillus subtilis*   *Staphylococcus epidermidis*   Tooth and gum scraping

Total
magnification: ___×   ___×   ___×

Morphology and
arrangement: _____   _____   _____

Questions

1. Which cell is a rod? _____ How does its appearance differ from the rod you

    stained with methylene blue (simple stain)? _____

2. Why is the size more accurate in a negative stain than in a simple stain? _____

    _____

3. Could any dye be used in place of nigrosin for negative staining? _____ What types of dyes are used for

    negative staining? _____ Briefly explain. _____

    _____

Critical Thinking

1. What microscopic technique gives a field similar in appearance to that seen in the negative stain?

2. Carbolfuchsin can be used as a simple stain and as a negative stain. As a simple stain, the pH is _____.

3. India ink can give the appearance of a negative stain when used in a wet mount. What is the basis (e.g., pH) for this stain? (India ink is a suspension of 0.5–1.0 μm carbon particles in water.)

Gram Staining

Objectives

After completing this exercise, you should be able to:

1. Explain the rationale and procedure for the Gram stain.
2. Perform and interpret Gram stains.

Background

The Gram stain is a useful stain for identifying and classifying bacteria. The **Gram stain** is a differential stain that allows you to classify bacteria as either gram-positive or gram-negative. The Gram-staining technique was discovered by Hans Christian Gram in 1884, when he attempted to stain cells and found that some lost their color when excess stain was washed off.

The staining technique consists of the following steps:

1. Apply **primary stain** (crystal violet). All bacteria are stained purple by this basic dye.
2. Apply **mordant** (Gram's iodine). The iodine combines with the crystal violet in the cell to form a crystal violet–iodine complex (CV–I).
3. Apply **decolorizing agent** (ethyl alcohol or ethyl alcohol–acetone). The primary stain is washed out (decolorized) of some bacteria, while others are unaffected.
4. Apply **secondary stain** or **counterstain** (safranin). This basic dye stains the decolorized bacteria red.

The most important determining factor in the procedure is that bacteria differ in their *rate* of decolorization. Those that decolorize easily are referred to as **gram-negative,** whereas those that decolorize slowly and retain the primary stain are called **gram-positive.**

Bacteria stain differently because of chemical and physical differences in their cell walls. Crystal violet is picked up by the cell. Iodine reacts with the dye in the cytoplasm to form a CV–I that is larger than the crystal violet that entered the cell. The CV–I cannot be washed out of gram-positive cells. In gram-negative cells, the decolorizing agent dissolves the outer lipopolysaccharide layer, and the CV–I washes out through the thin layer of peptidoglycan.

The Gram stain is most consistent when done on young cultures of bacteria (less than 24 hours old).

When bacteria die, their cell walls degrade and may not retain the primary stain, giving inaccurate results. Because Gram staining is usually the first step in identifying bacteria, the procedure should be memorized.

Materials

Gram-staining reagents:

    Crystal violet

    Gram's iodine

    Ethyl alcohol

    Safranin

Wash bottle of distilled water

Slides (3)

Cultures

Staphylococcus epidermidis

Escherichia coli

Bacillus subtilis

Techniques Required

Compound light microscopy

Smear preparation

Simple staining

Procedure (Figure 1)

1. Prepare and fix smears. Clean the slides well, and make a circle on each slide with a marker. Label each slide for one of the cultures.
2. Prepare a Gram stain of one smear. Use a clothespin or slide rack to hold the slides.
   a. Cover the smear with crystal violet and leave it for ~~30 seconds~~ 1 minute (Figure 1a).
   b. Wash the slide carefully with distilled water from a wash bottle. Do not squirt water directly onto the smear (Figure 1b).
   c. Cover the smear with Gram's iodine for 10 seconds (Figure 1c).

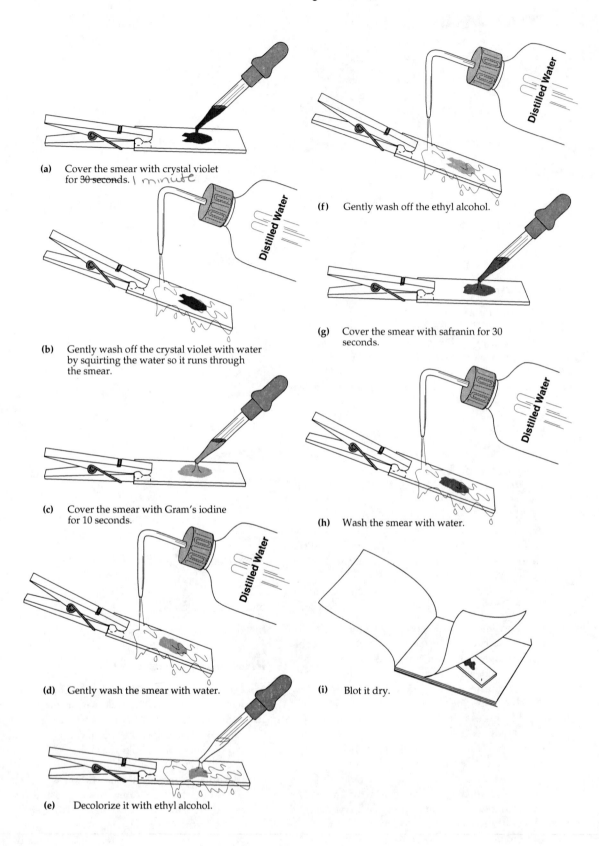

(a) Cover the smear with crystal violet for ~~30 seconds.~~ 1 minute

(b) Gently wash off the crystal violet with water by squirting the water so it runs through the smear.

(c) Cover the smear with Gram's iodine for 10 seconds.

(d) Gently wash the smear with water.

(e) Decolorize it with ethyl alcohol.

(f) Gently wash off the ethyl alcohol.

(g) Cover the smear with safranin for 30 seconds.

(h) Wash the smear with water.

(i) Blot it dry.

Figure 1
The Gram stain.

d. Wash off the iodine by tilting the slide and squirting water above the smear so that the water runs over the smear (Figure 1d).

e. Decolorize it with 95% ethyl alcohol (Figure 1e). Let the alcohol run through the smear until no large amounts of purple wash out (usually 10 to 20 seconds). The degree of decolorizing depends on the thickness of the smear. This is a critical step. *Do not overdecolorize.* However, experience is the only way you will be able to determine how long to decolorize. Very thick smears will give inaccurate results. Why? _____

_____

f. Immediately wash gently with distilled water (Figure 1f). Why? _____

g. Add safranin for 30 seconds (Figure 1g).

h. Wash the slide with distilled water and blot it dry with a paper towel or absorbent paper (Figure 1h and i).

3. Repeat step 2 to stain your remaining slides.

4. Examine the stained slides microscopically, using the low, high-dry, and oil immersion objectives. Put the oil directly on the smear. Record your observations. Do they agree with those given in your textbook? _____

If not, try to determine why. Some common sources of Gram-staining errors are the following:

a. The loop was too hot.

b. Excessive heat was applied during heat fixing.

c. The decolorizing agent (ethyl alcohol) was left on the smear too long.

d. The culture was too old.

e. The smear was too thick.

Acid-Fast Staining

Objectives

After completing this exercise, you should be able to:

1. Apply the acid-fast procedure.
2. Explain what is occurring during the acid-fast staining procedure.
3. Perform and interpret an acid-fast stain.

Background

The **acid-fast stain** is a differential stain. In 1882, Paul Ehrlich discovered that *Mycobacterium tuberculosis* (the causative agent of tuberculosis) retained the primary stain even after washing with an acid-alcohol mixture. (We hope you can appreciate the phenomenal strides that were made in microbiology in the 1880s. Most of the staining and culturing techniques used today originated during that time.) Most bacteria are decolorized by acid-alcohol, with only the families Mycobacteriaceae, Nocardiaceae, Gordoniaceae, Dietziaceae, and Tsukamurellaceae (*Bergey's Manual**) being acid-fast. The acid-fast technique has great value as a diagnostic procedure because both *Mycobacterium* and *Nocardia* contain **pathogenic** (disease-causing) species.

The cell walls of acid-fast organisms contain a wax-like lipid called **mycolic acid,** which renders the cell wall impermeable to most stains. The cell wall is so impermeable, in fact, that a clinical specimen is usually treated with strong sodium hydroxide to remove debris and contaminating bacteria prior to culturing mycobacteria. The mycobacteria are not killed by this procedure.

Today, the techniques developed by Franz Ziehl and Friedrich Neelsen and by Joseph J. Kinyoun are the most widely used acid-fast stains. In the **Ziehl–Neelsen procedure,** the smear is flooded with carbolfuchsin (a dark red dye containing 5% phenol), which has a high affinity for a chemical component of the bacterial cell. The smear is heated to facilitate penetration of the stain into the bacteria. The stained smears are washed with an acid-alcohol mixture that easily decolorizes most bacteria except the acid-fast microbes. Methylene blue is then used as a counterstain to enable you to observe the non-acid-fast organisms. In the **Kinyoun modification,** called a *cold stain,* the concentrations of phenol and carbolfuchsin are increased so heating isn't necessary.

The mechanism of the acid-fast stain is probably the result of the relative solubility of carbolfuchsin and the impermeability of the cell wall. Fuchsin is more soluble in carbolic acid (phenol) than in water, and carbolic acid solubilizes more easily in lipids than in acid-alcohol. Therefore, carbolfuchsin has a higher affinity for lipids than for acid-alcohol and will remain with the cell wall when washed with acid-alcohol.

Materials

Acid-fast staining reagents:

Kinyoun's carbolfuchsin

Acid-alcohol

Methylene blue

Wash bottle of distilled water

Slide

Cultures

Mycobacterium phlei rod shaped red

Escherichia coli blue.

Demonstration Slides

Acid-fast sputum slides

Techniques Required

Compound light microscopy

Smear preparation

Simple staining

Procedure (Figure 1)

1. Prepare and fix a smear of each culture.
2. Cover the smears with carbolfuchsin and let the smears stand for 5 minutes (Figure 1a).
3. Gently wash the slide with distilled water from a wash bottle. Do not squirt water directly onto the smear (Figure 1b).

---

*Bergey's Manual of Systematic Bacteriology, 2nd ed., 5 vols. (2005), is the standard reference for classification of prokaryotic organisms. Bergey's Manual of Determinative Bacteriology, 9th ed. (1994), is the standard reference for identification of culturable bacteria and archaea.

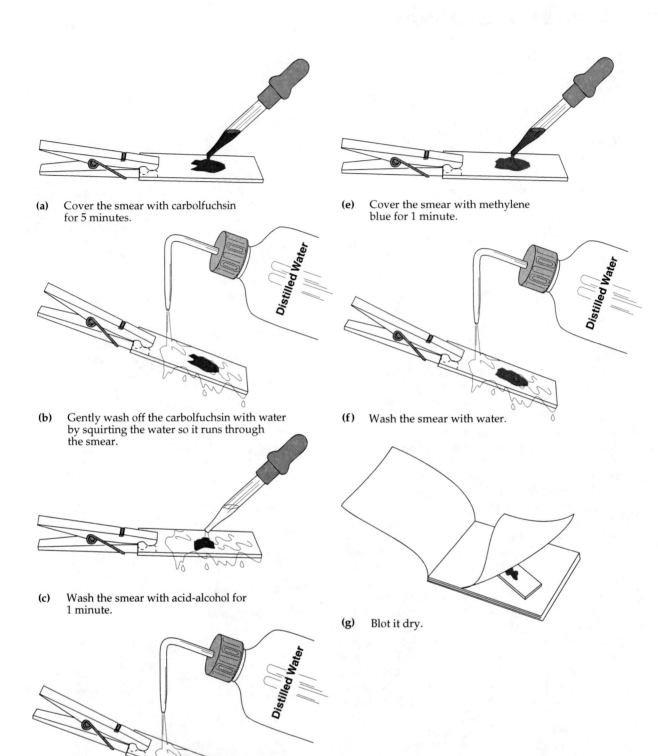

(a) Cover the smear with carbolfuchsin for 5 minutes.

(b) Gently wash off the carbolfuchsin with water by squirting the water so it runs through the smear.

(c) Wash the smear with acid-alcohol for 1 minute.

(d) Gently wash the smear with water.

(e) Cover the smear with methylene blue for 1 minute.

(f) Wash the smear with water.

(g) Blot it dry.

Figure 1

The acid-fast stain.

4. Without drying it, wash the smear with decolorizer (acid-alcohol) for 1 minute or until no more red color runs off when the slide is tipped (Figure 1c).

5. Wash the smear carefully with distilled water (Figure 1d).

6. Counterstain the smear for about 1 minute with methylene blue (Figure 1e).

7. Wash the smear with distilled water and blot it dry (Figure 1f and g).

8. Examine the acid-fast stained slide microscopically and record your observations.

9. Observe the demonstration slides.

LABORATORY REPORT

Acid-Fast Staining

NAME _____

DATE _____

LAB SECTION _____

Purpose _____ Identify bacteria w/ mycolic acid instead of
_____ peptidoglycan. Find mycobacterium vs any other bacteria.
(Red)   (blue)

Data

Sketch a few bacteria (oil immersion objective lens).

◯	◯

Bacteria: *Mycobacterium phlei*   *Escherichia coli*

Total magnification: ____×   ____×

Morphology: _____   _____

Acid-fast reaction: _____   _____

Demonstration Slide 1   Demonstration Slide 2

◯	◯

Specimen: _____   _____

Total magnification: ____×   ____×

Morphology: _____   _____

Acid-fast reaction: _____   _____

Questions

1. What are the large stained areas on the sputum slide? _No sputum slides available_

_____

_____

2. What is the decolorizing agent in the Gram stain? _Ethyl Alcohol_

   In the acid-fast stain? _Acid- Alcohol_

3. What diseases are diagnosed using the acid-fast procedure? _Tuberculosis. And other_
acid-fast   Mycobacterium ; Nocardia

4. What is phenol (carbolic acid), and what is its *usual* application? _Solubilize Carbofuschin_

_____

_____

Critical Thinking

1. How might the acid-fast characteristic of *Mycobacterium* enhance the organism's ability to cause disease?

   Mycolic Acid acting as a lipid barrier would prevent
   alysis

2. Clinical specimens suspected of containing *Mycobacterium* are digested with sodium hydroxide (NaOH) for 30 minutes prior to staining. Why is this technique used? Why isn't this technique used for staining other bacteria?

3. The acid-fast stain is used to detect *Cryptosporidium* protozoa in fecal samples. Which of the following would you expect to be a major component of their cell walls: carbohydrates, lipids, or proteins? _____

   What disease is caused by *Cryptosporidium*? _____

4. In 1882, after experimenting with staining *Mycobacterium*, Paul Ehrlich wrote that only alkaline disinfectants would be effective against *Mycobacterium*. How did he reach this conclusion without testing the disinfectants?

Acid-Fast Staining

NAME _____

DATE _____

LAB SECTION _____

Purpose _____

_____

_____

Data

Sketch a few bacteria (oil immersion objective lens).

◯	◯

Bacteria: *Mycobacterium phlei*   *Escherichia coli*

Total magnification: ___×   ___×

Morphology: _____   _____

Acid-fast reaction: _____   _____

Demonstration Slide 1	Demonstration Slide 2
◯	◯

Specimen: _____   _____

Total magnification: ___×   ___×

Morphology: _____   _____

Acid-fast reaction: _____   _____

Questions

1. What are the large stained areas on the sputum slide? _____

    _____

    _____

2. What is the decolorizing agent in the Gram stain? _____

    In the acid-fast stain? _____

3. What diseases are diagnosed using the acid-fast procedure? _____

    _____

4. What is phenol (carbolic acid), and what is its *usual* application? _____

    _____

    _____

Critical Thinking

1. How might the acid-fast characteristic of *Mycobacterium* enhance the organism's ability to cause disease?

2. Clinical specimens suspected of containing *Mycobacterium* are digested with sodium hydroxide (NaOH) for 30 minutes prior to staining. Why is this technique used? Why isn't this technique used for staining other bacteria?

3. The acid-fast stain is used to detect *Cryptosporidium* protozoa in fecal samples. Which of the following would you expect to be a major component of their cell walls: carbohydrates, lipids, or proteins? _____

    What disease is caused by *Cryptosporidium*? _____

4. In 1882, after experimenting with staining *Mycobacterium*, Paul Ehrlich wrote that only alkaline disinfectants would be effective against *Mycobacterium*. How did he reach this conclusion without testing the disinfectants?

Structural Stains (Endospore, Capsule, and Flagella)

Objectives

After completing this exercise, you should be able to:

1. Prepare and interpret endospore, capsule, and flagella stains.
2. Recognize the different types of flagellar arrangements.
3. Identify functions of endospores, capsules, and flagella.

Background

Structural stains can be used to identify and study the structure of bacteria. Currently, most of the fine structural details are examined using an electron microscope, but historically, staining techniques have given much insight into bacterial fine structure. We will examine a few structural stains that are still useful today. These stains are used to observe endospores, capsules, and flagella.

Endospores

Endospores are formed by several genera in the orders Bacillales and Clostridiales.* *Bacillus* and *Clostridium* are the most familiar genera. Endospores are called "resting bodies" because they do not metabolize and are resistant to heating, various chemicals, and many harsh environmental conditions. Endospores are not for reproduction; they are formed when essential nutrients or water are not available. Once an endospore forms in a cell, the cell will disintegrate (Figure 1a). Endospores can remain dormant for long periods of time. However, an endospore may return to its vegetative or growing state.

Taxonomically, it is helpful to know whether a bacterium is an endospore former and also the position of the endospores (Figure 1b through e). Endospores are impermeable to most stains so heat is usually applied to drive the stain into the endospore. Once stained, the endospores do not readily decolorize. We will use the **Schaeffer–Fulton** endospore stain.

Bergey's Manual of Systematic Bacteriology, 2nd ed. (2005).

Capsules

Many bacteria secrete chemicals that adhere to their surfaces, forming a viscous coat. This structure is called a **capsule** when it is round or oval in shape, and a **slime layer** when it is irregularly shaped and loosely bound to the bacterium. The ability to form capsules is genetically determined, but the size of the capsule is influenced by the medium on which the bacterium is growing. Most capsules are composed of polysaccharides, which are water soluble and uncharged. Because of the capsule's nonionic nature, simple stains will not adhere to it. Most capsule-staining techniques stain the bacteria and the background, leaving the capsules unstained—essentially, a "negative" capsule stain.

Capsules have an important role in the **virulence** (disease-causing ability) of some bacteria. For example, when bacteria such as *Streptococcus pneumoniae* have a capsule, the body's white blood cells cannot phagocytize the bacteria efficiently, and disease occurs. When *S. pneumoniae* lack a capsule, they are easily engulfed and are not virulent.

Flagella

Many bacteria are **motile,** which means they have the ability to move from one position to another in a directed manner. Most motile bacteria possess flagella, but other forms of motility occur. Myxobacteria exhibit gliding motion, and spirochetes undulate using axial filaments.

Flagella, the most common means of motility, are thin proteinaceous structures that originate in the cytoplasm and project out from the cell wall. They are very fragile and are not visible with a light microscope. They can be stained after carefully coating them using a mordant, which increases their diameter. The presence and location of flagella are helpful in the identification and classification of bacteria. Flagella are of two main types: **peritrichous** (all around the bacterium) and **polar** (at one or both ends of the cell) (Figure 2).

Motility may be determined by observing hanging-drop or wet-mount preparations of unstained bacteria, flagella stains, or inoculation of soft (or semisolid) agar deeps. If time does not permit doing flagella stains, observe the demonstration slides.

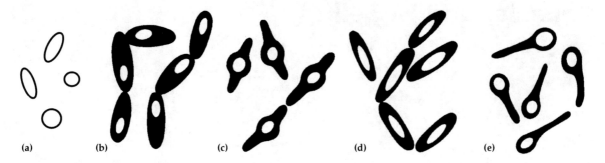

Figure 1

Some examples of bacterial endospores. (a) Free endospores after the cell has disintegrated. (b) Subterminal endospores (*Bacillus macerans*). (c) Central, swollen endospores (*Clostridium perfringens*). (d) Central endospores (*Bacillus polymyxa*). (e) Terminal, swollen endospores (*Clostridium tetani*).

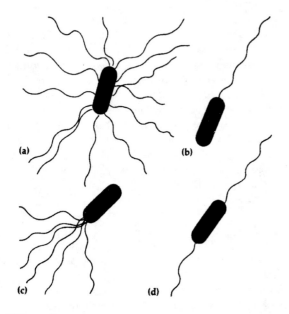

Figure 2

Flagellar arrangements. (a) Peritrichous flagella. Types of polar flagella: (b) monotrichous flagella, (c) lophotrichous flagella, and (d) amphitrichous flagella.

Materials

Slides

Coverslips

Paper towels

Wash bottle of distilled water

Forceps

Scalpel

Beaker with alcohol

Endospore stain reagents: malachite green and safranin

Capsule stain reagents: Congo red, acid-alcohol, and acid fuchsin

Flagella stain reagents: flagella mordant and carbolfuchsin

Cultures (as needed)

Endospore stain:

    Bacillus megaterium (24-hour)

    Bacillus subtilis (24-hour)

    Bacillus subtilis (72-hour)

Capsule stain:

    Streptococcus salivarius

    Enterobacter aerogenes

Flagella stain:

    Proteus vulgaris (18-hour)

Demonstration Slides

Endospore stain

Capsule stain

Flagella stain

Techniques Required

Compound light microscopy

Smear preparation

Simple staining

Negative staining

Procedure

Endospore Stain (Figure 3)

Be careful. The malachite green has a messy habit of ending up everywhere. But most likely you will end up with green fingers no matter how careful you are.

1. Make smears of the three *Bacillus* cultures on one or two slides, let them air-dry, and heat-fix them.
2. Tear out small pieces of paper towel and place them on each smear to reduce evaporation of the stain. The paper should be smaller than the slide (Figure 3a).
3. Cover the smears and paper with malachite green; steam the slide for 5 minutes. Add more stain as needed. *Keep it wet* (Figure 3b and c). What is the purpose of the paper? _____
4. Remove the towel and discard it carefully. *Do not put it in the sink.* Wash the stained smears well with distilled water (Figure 3d).
5. Counterstain with safranin for 30 seconds (Figure 3e).
6. Wash the smear with distilled water and blot it dry (Figure 3f).
7. Examine the slide microscopically and record your observations.
8. Observe the demonstration slides of the bacterial endospores.

Capsule Stain (Figure 4)

1. Draw two circles on a slide. Place a loopful of Congo red in each circle (Figure 4a).
2. Prepare a thick smear of *S. salivarius* in the Congo red in one circle. Prepare a thick smear of *E. aerogenes* in the other circle. Let the smears air-dry (Figure 4b and c). What color are the smears?

   _____
3. Fix the smears with acid-alcohol for 15 seconds (Figure 4d). What color are the smears? _____
4. Wash the smears with distilled water and cover them with acid fuchsin for 1 minute (Figure 4e and f).

5. Wash the smears with distilled water and blot them dry (Figure 4g).
6. Examine the slide microscopically. The bacteria will stain red, and the capsules will be colorless against a dark blue background. Record your observations.
7. Observe the demonstration slides of capsule stains.

Flagella Stain (Figure 5)

1. Flagella stains require special precautions to avoid damaging the flagella. Scrupulously clean slides are essential, and the culture must be handled carefully to prevent flagella from coming off the cells.
2. Without touching the bacterial culture, use a scalpel and forceps to cut out a piece of agar on which *Proteus* is growing (Figure 5a).

   +---+
   | **Do not touch the culture with your hands.** |
   +---+

   Gently place the agar, culture-side down, on a clean glass slide (Figure 5b). Then carefully remove the agar with the forceps. Place the piece of agar in a Petri plate. Place the forceps and scalpel in alcohol.
3. Allow the organisms adhering to the slide to air-dry. *Do not heat-fix the slide* (Figure 5c).
4. Cover the slide with flagella mordant and allow it to stand for 10 minutes (Figure 5d).
5. Gently rinse off the stain with distilled water (Figure 5e).
6. Cover the slide with carbolfuchsin for 5 minutes (Figure 5f). Rinse it gently with distilled water (Figure 5g). What color should the flagella be?

   _____

   The cells? _____
7. Allow the rinsed smear to air-dry (*do not blot it*), and examine it microscopically for flagella.
8. Observe the demonstration slides illustrating various flagellar arrangements.

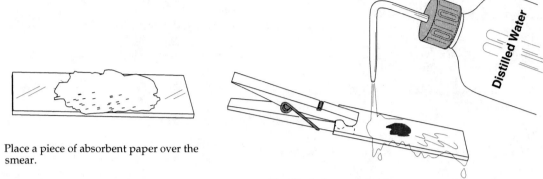

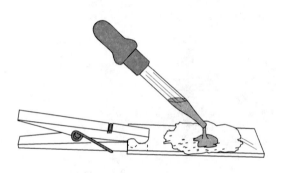

(a) Place a piece of absorbent paper over the smear.

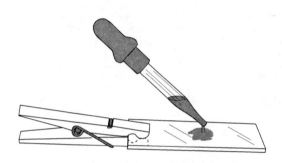

(d) Wash the smear with water.

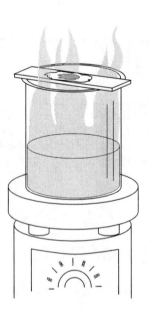

(b) Cover the paper with malachite green.

(e) Cover the smear with safranin for 30 seconds.

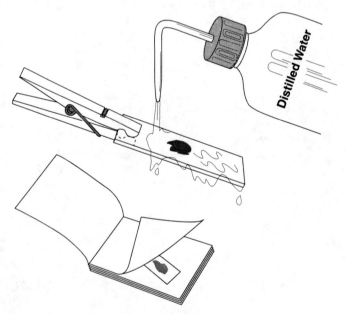

(c) Steam the slide for 5 minutes.

(f) Wash the smear with water and blot it dry.

Figure 3

The endospore stain.

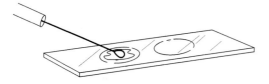

(a)   Place one loopful of Congo red in each circle.

(b)   Prepare a thick smear of bacteria in the Congo red.

(c)   Allow the smears to air-dry.

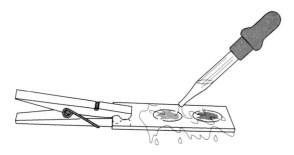

(d)   Cover each smear with acid-alcohol for 15 seconds.

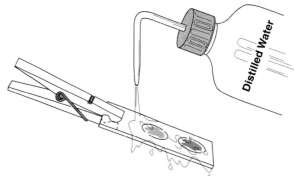

(e)   Wash the smears with water.

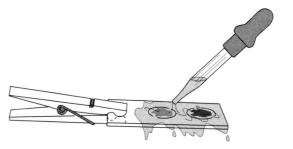

(f)   Cover the smears with acid fuchsin for 1 minute.

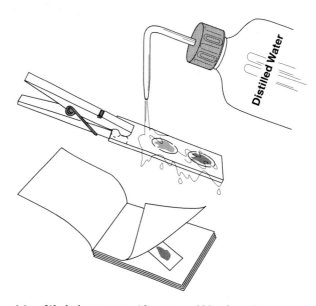

(g)   Wash the smears with water and blot them dry.

Figure 4

The capsule stain.

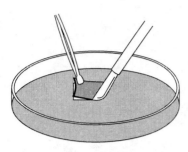

(a) Carefully cut a piece of the bacterial culture.

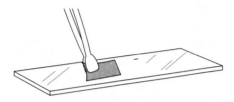

(b) Gently touch the culture side of the agar piece to a clean slide.

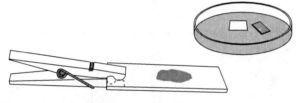

(c) Allow the imprint to air-dry.

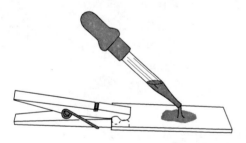

(d) Cover the slide with flagella mordant for 10 minutes.

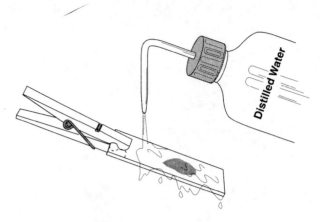

(e) Gently rinse the slide with water.

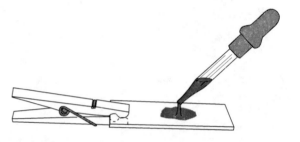

(f) Cover the slide with carbolfuchsin for 5 minutes.

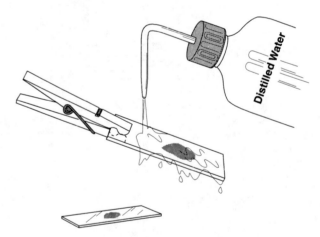

(g) Gently rinse the slide with water and let it air-dry.

Figure 5
The flagella stain.

LABORATORY REPORT

Structural Stains (Endospore, Capsule, and Flagella)

NAME _Ashley Myers_

DATE _____

LAB SECTION _____

Purpose _to be able to prepare endospore stains,_
+ identify functions as endospers

Data

Endospores

Sketch your results, and label the color in each diagram. Label the vegetative cells and endospores.

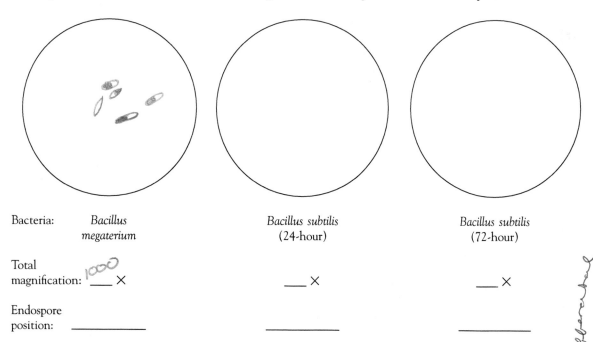

Bacteria:	*Bacillus megaterium*	*Bacillus subtilis* (24-hour)	*Bacillus subtilis* (72-hour)

Total magnification: 1000 ___ ×   ___ ×   ___ ×

Endospore position: _____   _____   _____

selective differential
antibiotic
gram
acid fast

Demonstration Slides

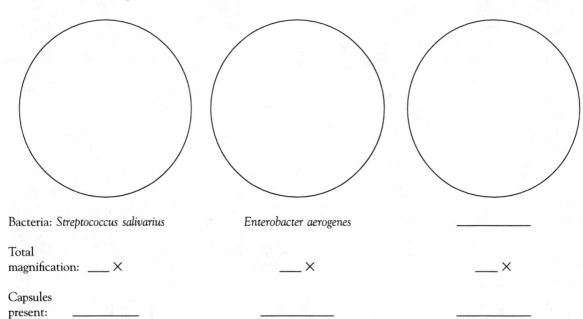

Bacteria: _____   _____   _____

Total
magnification: ___ ✕   ___ ✕   ___ ✕

Endospore
position: _____   _____   _____

Capsules

Sketch and label the capsules and bacterial cells.   Demonstration Slide

Bacteria: *Streptococcus salivarius*   *Enterobacter aerogenes*   _____

Total
magnification: ___ ✕   ___ ✕   ___ ✕

Capsules
present: _____   _____   _____

Flagella

Sketch and label the flagella and bacteria.   Demonstration Slides

Bacteria: *Proteus vulgaris*   _____   _____

Total
magnification: ___ ✕   ___ ✕   ___ ✕

Flagella
position: _____   _____   _____

Questions

1. What are the Gram reactions of *Clostridium* and *Bacillus*? _____

   _____

2. How might a capsule contribute to pathogenicity? _____

   How might flagella contribute to pathogenicity? _____

3. Of what advantage to *Clostridium* is an endospore? _____

   _____

   _____

4. Sketch each of the following flagellar arrangements:

   a. Monotrichous

   b. Lophotrichous

   c. Amphitrichous

   d. Peritrichous

5. How did the appearance of the 24-hour and 72-hour *Bacillus* cultures differ? How do you account for this difference? _The appearace differs because in the 72 hour there were many more endospores broken away from the shells of the cell._

6. Of what morphology are most bacteria possessing flagella? _____

   Which morphology usually does not have flagella? _____

7. What prevents the cell from appearing green in the finished endospore stain? _____

   _____

   _____

Critical Thinking

1. You can see endospores by simple staining. Why not use this technique?

2. How would an endospore stain of *Mycobacterium* appear?

3. What type of culture medium would increase the size of a bacterial capsule?

4. Describe the microscopic appearance of encapsulated *Streptococcus* if stained with safranin and nigrosin.

5. In the Dorner endospore stain, a smear covered with carbolfuchsin is steamed, then decolorized with acid-alcohol and counterstained with nigrosin. Describe the microscopic appearance after this procedure.

Morphologic Unknown

Dishonesty is knowing but ignoring the fact that the data are contradictory.
Stupidity is not recognizing the contradictions.

Anonymous

Objective

After completing this exercise, you should be able to identify the morphology and staining characteristics of an unknown organism.

Background

Differential staining is usually the first step in the identification of bacteria. Morphology and structural characteristics obtained from microscopic examination are also useful for identification. *Bergey's Manual** is the most widely used reference for bacterial identification. In *Bergey's Manual*, bacteria are identified by differential staining, morphology, and several other characteristics. Additional testing is needed to identify bacterial species. You will learn these techniques later in this course.

You will be given an unknown culture of bacteria. Determine its morphologic and structural characteristics. The culture contains one species (rod or coccus) and is less than 24 hours old.

Quality control (QC) is an essential component of the microbiology laboratory. The accuracy of information from stains and other tests depends on a variety of factors, including the specimen, reagents, procedures, and the person doing the test. Generally during staining, known positive and negative bacteria are stained at the same time as unknown bacteria as a check on reagents and procedures.

---

*Bergey's Manual of Systematic Bacteriology, 2nd ed., 5 vols. (2001), is the standard reference for classification of prokaryotic organisms. Bergey's Manual of Determinative Bacteriology, 9th ed. (1994), is the standard reference for identification of culturable bacteria and archaea.

Materials

Staining reagents

Culture

24-hour unknown slant culture of bacteria #_____

Techniques Required

Compound light microscopy

Hanging-drop and wet-mount procedures

Smear preparation

Simple staining

Negative staining

Gram staining

Acid-fast staining

Endospore, capsule, and flagella staining

Procedure

1. Record the number of your unknown in your Laboratory Report.
2. Determine the morphology, Gram reaction, and arrangement of your unknown. Perform a Gram stain and, if needed, an endospore stain, acid-fast stain, flagella stain, hanging-drop technique, and capsule stain. When are the latter needed? _____
3. Tabulate your results in the Laboratory Report.

Morphologic Unknown

NAME _____

DATE _____

LAB SECTION _____

Results

Write *not necessary* by any category that does not apply.

Unknown # _____

Gram Stain

Sketch your unknown.

Specimen:	*Staphylococcus epidermidis*	*Escherichia coli*	Unknown
Total magnification:	___ ×	___ ×	___ ×
Gram reaction:	_____	_____	_____
Morphology:	_____	_____	_____
Predominant arrangement:	_____	_____	_____

Acid-Fast Stain

Sketch your unknown.

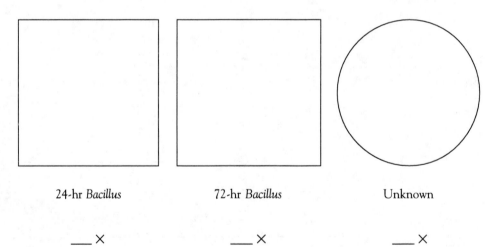

Specimen:	*Mycobacterium phlei*	*Escherichia coli*	Unknown

Total
magnification: ___ ✕   ___ ✕   ___ ✕

Acid-fast reaction: _____ _____ _____

Endospore Stain

Sketch your unknown.

Specimen:	24-hr *Bacillus*	72-hr *Bacillus*	Unknown

Total
magnification: ___ ✕   ___ ✕   ___ ✕

Endospores present: _____ _____ _____

Capsule Stain

Sketch your unknown.

Specimen:	*Streptococcus salivarius* Unknown
Total magnification:	___ × ___ ×
Capsules present:	_____ _____

Motility

Is your unknown motile? _____

How did you determine this? _____

Questions

1. Which two stains done in this experiment are differential stains? _____

    _____

2. Assume you have performed a Gram stain on a sample of pus from a patient's urethra. You see red, nucleated

    cells (>10 μm) and purple rods (2.5 μm). What can you conclude? _____

    _____

    _____

Critical Thinking

1. Using *Bergey's Manual* and your textbook, place the following genera in this flowchart: *Bacillus, Corynebacterium, Escherichia, Mycobacterium, Neisseria, Sporosarcina,* and *Staphylococcus*.

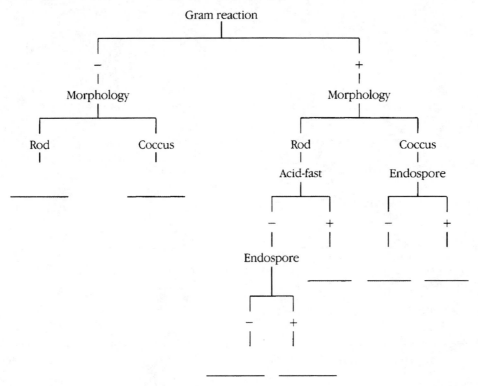

2. Which genera listed in the previous question should you test for capsules? For motility?

3. Using your textbook and this lab manual, fill in the Morphology column in the following table. Then use the information to construct a flowchart for these bacteria. Draw your flowchart in the space below the table.

	Morphology	Gram Reaction	Motile	Capsule	Arrangement	Endospore
Clostridium		+	+	−	Pairs, chains	+
Enterobacter		−	+	−	Singles, pairs	−
Klebsiella		−	−	+	Singles, pairs	−
Lactobacillus		+	Rarely	−	Chains	−
Staphylococcus		+	−	−	Pairs, clusters	−
Streptococcus		+	−	Some species	Pairs, chains	−

4. Provide an example from the previous question to show that microscopic examination alone cannot be used to identify bacteria.

Microbes in the Environment

Whatever is worth doing at all is worth doing well.

Philip Dormer Stanhope

Objectives

After completing this exercise, you should be able to:

1. Describe why agar is used in culture media.
2. Prepare nutrient broth and nutrient agar.
3. Compare bacterial growth on solid and liquid culture media.
4. Describe colony morphology using accepted descriptive terms.

Background

Microbes are everywhere; they are found in the water we drink, the air we breathe, and the earth on which we walk. They live in and on our bodies. Microbes occupy ecological niches on all forms of life and in most environments. In most situations, the ubiquitous microorganisms are harmless. However, in microbiology, work must be done carefully to avoid contaminating sterile media and materials with these microbes.

In this exercise, we will attempt to culture (grow) some microbes from the environment. When a medium is selected for culturing bacteria, macronutrients, an energy source, and any necessary growth factors must be provided. A medium whose exact chemical composition is known is called a **chemically defined medium** (Table 1).

Most chemoheterotrophic bacteria are routinely grown on **complex media**—that is, media for which the exact chemical composition varies slightly from batch to batch. Organic carbon, energy, and nitrogen sources are usually supplied by protein in the form of meat extracts and partially digested proteins called *peptones*. **Nutrient broth** is a commonly used liquid complex medium. When agar is added, it becomes a solid medium, called **nutrient agar** (Table 2).

Agar, an extract from marine red algae, has some unique properties that make it useful in culture media. Few microbes can degrade agar so it remains solid during microbial growth. It liquefies at 100°C and remains in a liquid state until cooled to 40°C. Once the agar has solidified, it can be incubated at temperatures of up to 100°C and remain solid.

Media must be sterilized after preparation. The most common method of sterilizing culture media that are heat stable is **steam sterilization,** or **autoclaving,** using steam under pressure. During this process, material to be sterilized is placed in the autoclave and heated to 121°C at 15 pounds of pressure (15 psi) for 15 minutes.

Culture media can be prepared in various forms, depending on the desired use. **Petri plates** containing solid media provide a large surface area for examination of colonies. The microbes will be **inoculated,** or intentionally introduced, onto nutrient agar and into nutrient broth. The bacteria that are inoculated into culture

Table 1

Glucose–Minimal Salts Broth

Ingredient	Amount/100 ml
Glucose	0.5 g
Sodium chloride (NaCl)	0.5 g
Ammonium dihydrogen phosphate ($NH_4H_2PO_4$)	0.1 g
Dipotassium phosphate (K_2HPO_4)	0.1 g
Magnesium sulfate ($MgSO_4$)	0.02 g
Distilled water	100 ml

Table 2

Nutrient Agar

Ingredient	Amount/100 ml
Peptone	0.5 g
Beef extract	0.3 g
Sodium chloride (NaCl)	0.8 g
Agar	1.5 g
Distilled water	100 ml

media increase in number during an **incubation period.** After suitable incubation, liquid media become **turbid,** or cloudy, due to bacterial growth. On solid media, colonies will be visible to the naked eye. A **colony** is a population of cells that arises from a single bacterial cell. A colony may arise from a group of the same microbes attached to one another, which is therefore called a **colony-forming unit.** Although many species of bacteria give rise to colonies that appear similar, each colony that appears different is usually a different species.

Materials

250-ml Erlenmeyer flask with cap or plug

100-ml graduated cylinder

Distilled water

Nutrient broth powder

Agar

Glass stirring rod

5-ml pipette

Propipette or pipette bulb

Test tubes with caps (3)

Sterile Petri dishes (4)

Balance

Weighing paper or dish

Autoclave gloves

Hot plate

Tube containing sterile cotton swabs

Tube containing sterile water

Demonstration

Use of the autoclave

Techniques Required

Pipetting

Procedure

First Period

1. Preparing culture media
   a. Prepare 100 ml of nutrient broth in a 250-ml flask. Using the graduated cylinder, add 100 ml of distilled water to the flask. Read the preparation instructions on the nutrient broth bottle. Calculate the amount of nutrient broth powder needed for 100 ml. If the amount needed for 1000 ml is _____ grams, then _____ grams are needed for 100 ml. Weigh out the required amount and add it to the flask. Stir with a glass rod until the powder is dissolved.
   b. Attach a bulb or Propipette to the 5-ml pipette. Pipette 5 ml of the nutrient broth into each test tube and cap each tube. Label the tubes "nutrient broth." Place two in the To Be Autoclaved rack. Label the remaining tube "not sterilized," and incubate it at room temperature until the next period.
   c. Add agar (1.5% w/v) to the remaining 85 ml of nutrient broth. What quantity of agar will you need to add? _____
   d. Bring the broth to a boil and continue boiling carefully until all the agar is dissolved. *Be careful:* Do not let the solution boil over. Stir often to prevent burning and boiling over.
   e. Stopper the flask, label it "nutrient agar," and place the flask and tube in the To Be Autoclaved basket.
   f. Listen to the instructor's demonstration of the use of the autoclave.
   g. After autoclaving, allow the flasks and tube to cool to room temperature, or proceed to part 2. What effect does the agar have on the culture medium? _____
2. Pouring plates
   Transfer the melted sterile nutrient agar flasks to a 45°C water bath. Allow the flask of nutrient agar to cool to about 45°C (warm to the touch). If the agar has solidified, it will have to be reheated to liquefy it. To what temperature will it have to be heated? _____
   The sterile nutrient agar must be poured into Petri dishes *aseptically*—that is, without letting microbes into the nutrient medium. *Read the following procedure before beginning* so that you can work quickly and efficiently.
   a. Set four sterile, unopened Petri dishes in front of you with the cover (larger half) on top. Have a lighted laboratory burner within reach on your workbench.

 Keep the burner away from your hair and in the center of the bench.

---

   b. Holding the flask at an angle, remove the stopper with the fourth and fifth fingers of your other hand. Heat the mouth of the flask by passing it through the flame three times (Figure 1a). Why is it necessary to keep the flask at an angle through this procedure? _____

   _____

c. Remove the cover from the first dish with the hand holding the plug. Quickly and neatly pour melted nutrient agar into the dish until the bottom is just covered to a depth of approximately 5 mm (Figure 1b). Keep the flask at an angle, and replace the dish cover; move on to the next plate until all the agar is poured.

d. When all the agar is poured, gently swirl the agar in each dish to cover any empty spaces; do not allow the agar to touch the dish covers.

e. To decrease condensation, leave the Petri plate covers slightly ajar for about 15 minutes until the agar solidifies.

f. Place the empty flask in the discard area.

3. Culturing microbes from the environment

a. Design your own experiment. The purpose is to sample your environment and your body. Use your imagination. Here are some suggestions:

1. You may use the lab, a washroom, or any place on campus for the environment.

2. One nutrient agar plate might be left open to the air for 30 to 60 minutes.

3. Inoculate a plate from an environmental surface such as the floor or workbench by wetting a cotton swab in sterile water, swabbing the environmental surface, and then swabbing the surface of the agar. Why is the swab first moistened in sterile water?

_____

_____

After inoculation, the swab should be discarded in the container of disinfectant.

b. Inoculate two plates from the environment. Inoculate one nutrient broth tube using a swab as described in step 3 of 3a. After swabbing the agar surface, place the swab in the nutrient broth and leave it there during incubation. You may need to break off part of the wooden handle to fit the swab into the nutrient broth.

c. The plates and tube should be incubated at the approximate temperature of the environment sampled.

d. Inoculate two plates from your body. You could:

1. Place a hair on the agar.

2. Obtain an inoculum by swabbing (see step 3 of 3a) part of your body with a wet swab.

3. Touch the plate with your fingers.

e. Incubate bacteria from your body at or close to your body temperature. What is human body temperature? _____°C

f. Incubate all plates inverted, so water will condense in the lid instead of on the surface of the agar. Why is condensation on the agar undesirable? _____

_____

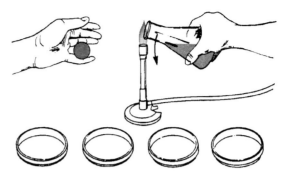

(a) Remove the stopper, and flame the mouth of the flask.

(b) Remove the cover from one dish, and pour nutrient agar into the dish bottom.

Figure 1

Petri plate pouring.

g. Incubate all inoculated media until the next laboratory period.

Second Period

1. Observe and describe the resulting growth on the plates. Note each different-appearing colony, and describe the colony pigment (color) and morphology using the characteristics given in Figure 2. Determine the approximate number of each type of colony. When many colonies are present, record TNTC (too numerous to count) as the number of colonies.

2. Describe the appearance of the nutrient broth labeled "not sterile" and the broth you inoculated. Are they uniformly cloudy or turbid? _____
Look for clumps of microbial cells, called **flocculent.** Is there a membrane, or **pellicle,** across the surface of the broth? _____ See whether microbial cells have settled on the bottom of the tube, forming a **sediment.**

3. Save one turbid broth in the refrigerator for Exercise 11. Discard the plates and remaining tubes properly.

 Place contaminated plates in the biohazard bag for autoclaving.

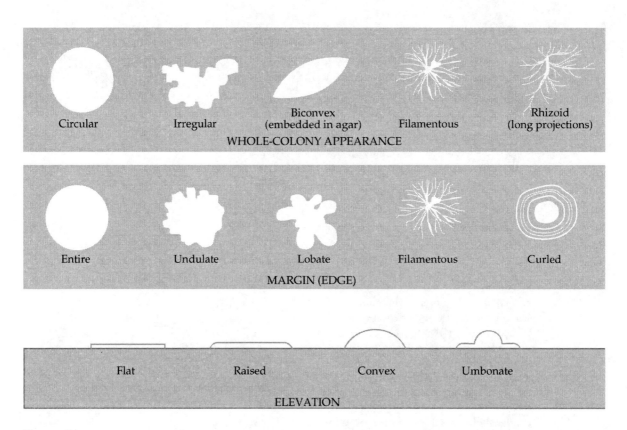

Figure 2

Colony descriptions.

Microbes in the Environment

NAME _____

DATE _____

LAB SECTION _____

Purpose _____

_____

_____

Data

Fill in the following table with descriptions of the bacterial colonies. Use a separate line for each different-appearing colony. Observe your classmates' plates if you didn't inoculate four plates.

	Colony Description					
	Diameter	Whole-Colony Appearance	Margin	Elevation	Pigment	Number of this Type
Area sampled: _____ Incubated at _____°C for _____ days						
Area sampled: _____ Incubated at _____°C for _____ days						
Area sampled: _____ Incubated at _____°C for _____ days						

	Colony Description					
	Diameter	Whole-Colony Appearance	Margin	Elevation	Pigment	Number of this Type
Area sampled: _____ Incubated at _____ °C for _____ days						

Nutrient broths: Incubated at _____ °C for _____ days

	Not-Sterilized Broth	Sterilized Broth Not Inoculated	Inoculated Broth Area Sampled: _____
Turbidity			
Flocculent present			
Sediment present			
Pellicle present			
Color			

Questions

1. How can you tell whether there is bacterial growth in the nutrient broth? _____

   _____

2. What is the minimum number of different bacteria present on one of your plates? _____

   How do you know? _____

   _____

3. What is the value of Petri plates in microbiology? _____

   _____

4. What are bacteria using for nutrients in nutrient agar? _____

_____

What is the purpose of the agar? _____

_____

5. Which environment has the most total bacteria? _____ The least? _____ Provide

a reason for the differences in total bacteria in these two places. _____

_____

_____

6. Which environment has the most different bacteria? _____ The least? _____

Provide a reason for the differences in bacteria in these two places. _____

_____

_____

Critical Thinking

1. Why is agar preferable to gelatin as a solidifying agent in culture media?

2. Did all the organisms living in or on the environments sampled grow on your nutrient agar? Briefly explain.

3. How could you determine whether the turbidity in your nutrient broth tube was from a mixture of different microbes or from the growth of only one kind of microbe?

Transfer of Bacteria: Aseptic Technique

Study without thinking is worthless; thinking without study is dangerous.

CONFUCIUS

Objectives

After completing this exercise, you should be able to:

1. Provide the rationale for aseptic technique.
2. Differentiate among the following: broth culture, agar slant, and agar deep.
3. Aseptically transfer bacteria from one form of culture medium to another.

Background

In the laboratory, bacteria must be cultured in order to facilitate identification and to examine their growth and metabolism. Bacteria are **inoculated,** or introduced, into various forms of culture media in order to keep them alive and to study their growth. Inoculations must be done without introducing unwanted microbes, or **contaminants,** into the media. **Aseptic technique** is used in microbiology to exclude contaminants.

All culture media are **sterilized,** or rendered free of all life, prior to use. Sterilization is usually accomplished using an autoclave. Containers of culture media, such as test tubes or Petri plates, should not be opened until you are ready to work with them, and even then, they should not be left open.

Broth cultures provide large numbers of bacteria in a small space and are easily transported. **Agar slants** are test tubes containing solid culture media that were left at an angle while the agar solidified. Agar slants, like Petri plates, provide a solid growth surface, but slants are easier to store and transport than Petri plates. Agar is allowed to solidify in the bottom of a test tube to make an **agar deep.** Deeps are often used to grow bacteria that require less oxygen than is present on the surface of the medium. Semisolid agar deeps containing 0.5–0.7% agar instead of the usual 1.5% agar can be used to determine whether a bacterium is motile. Motile bacteria will move away from the point of inoculation, giving the appearance of an inverted Christmas tree.

Aseptic transfer and inoculation are usually performed with a sterile, heat-resistant, noncorroding Nichrome wire attached to an insulated handle. When the end of the wire is bent into a loop, it is called an **inoculating loop;** when straight, it is an **inoculating needle** (Figure 1). For special purposes, cultures may also be transferred with sterile cotton swabs, pipettes, glass rods, or syringes. These techniques will be introduced in later exercises.

Whether to use an inoculating loop or a needle depends on the form of the medium; after completing this exercise, you will be able to decide which instrument is to be used.

Materials

Tubes containing nutrient broth (3)

Tubes containing nutrient agar slants (3)

Tubes containing nutrient semisolid agar deeps (3)

Inoculating loop

Inoculating needle

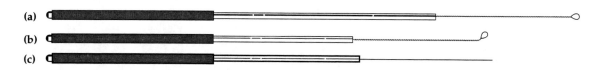

(a)
(b)
(c)

Figure 1

(a) An inoculating loop. **(b)** A variation of the inoculating loop in which the loop is bent at a 45° angle. **(c)** An inoculating needle.

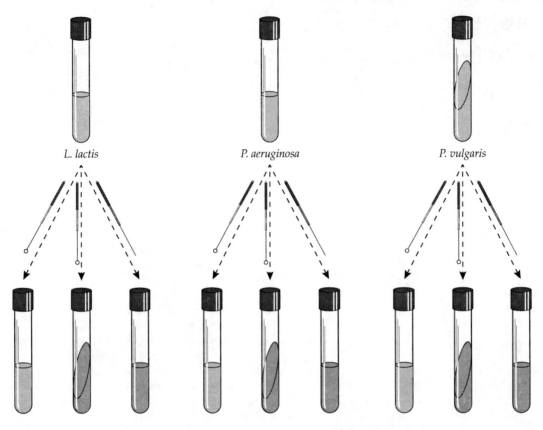

Figure 2

Inoculate one tube of each medium with each of the cultures using a loop or needle as indicated. Work with only one culture at a time to avoid contamination.

Test-tube rack

Gram-staining reagents

Cultures

Lactococcus lactis broth

Pseudomonas aeruginosa broth

Proteus vulgaris slant

Techniques Required

Compound light microscopy

Smear preparation

Gram staining

Procedure (Figure 2)

1. Work with only one of the bacterial cultures at a time to prevent any mix-ups or cross-contamination. Label one tube of each medium with the name of the first culture, your name, the date, and your lab section. Inoculate each tube as described and then work with the next culture. Begin with one of the broth cultures, and gently tap the bottom of it to resuspend the sediment.

2. To inoculate nutrient broth, hold the inoculating loop in your dominant hand and one of the broth cultures of bacteria in the other hand.

   a. Sterilize the loop by holding the wire in a Bunsen burner flame (Figure 3a). Heat to redness. Why? _____

   b. Holding the loop like a pencil or paintbrush, curl the little finger of the same hand around the cap of the broth culture. Gently pull the cap off the tube while turning the culture tube (Figure 3b). If cotton stoppers are used, simply grasp the stopper with your finger. Do not set down the cap. Why not? _____

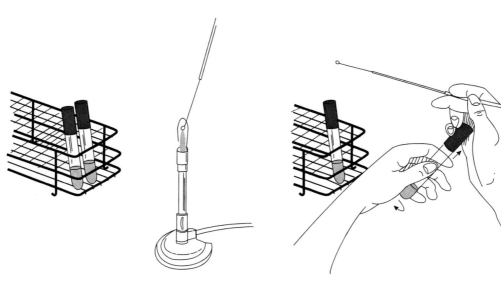

(a) Sterilize the loop by holding the wire in the flame until it is red-hot.

(b) While holding the sterile loop and the bacterial culture, remove the cap as shown.

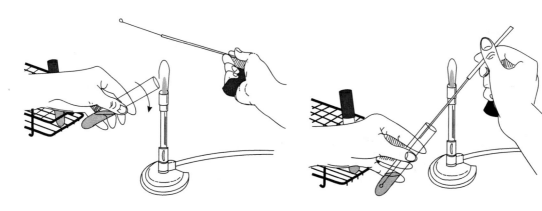

(c) Briefly pass the mouth of the tube through the flame three times before inserting the loop for an inoculum.

(d) Get a loopful of culture, heat the mouth of the tube, and replace the cap.

Figure 3

Inoculating procedures.

---

c. Holding the tube at an angle, pass the mouth of the tube through the flame three times (Figure 3c). What is the purpose of flaming the mouth of the tube? _____
Always hold culture tubes and uninoculated tubes at about a 20° angle to minimize the amount of dust that could fall into them. Do not tip the tube too far, or the liquid will leak out around the loose-fitting cap. Do not let the top edge of the tube touch anything.

d. Immerse the sterilized, cooled loop into the broth culture to obtain a loopful of culture (Figure 3d). Why must the loop be cooled first?

_____

Remove the loop, and while holding the loop, flame the mouth of the tube and recap it by turning the tube into the cap. Place the tube in your test-tube rack.

e. Remove the cap from a tube of sterile nutrient broth as previously described, and flame the

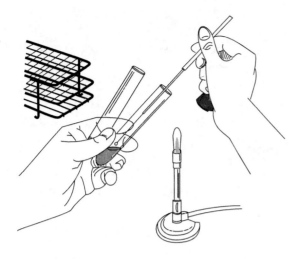

Figure 4

Experienced laboratory technicians can transfer cultures aseptically while holding multiple test tubes.

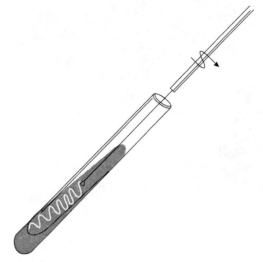

Figure 5

Inoculate a slant by streaking the loop back and forth across the surface of the agar.

mouth of the tube. Immerse the inoculating loop into the sterile broth and then withdraw it from the tube. Flame the mouth of the tube and replace the cap. Return the tube to the test-tube rack.

   f. Reflame the loop until it is red and let it cool. Some microbiologists prefer to hold several tubes in their hands at once (Figure 4). *Do not attempt holding and transferring between multiple tubes until you have mastered aseptic transfer techniques.*

3. Obtain a nutrient agar slant. Repeat steps 2a–2d, and inoculate the slant by moving the loop gently across the agar surface from the bottom of the slant to the top, being careful not to gouge the agar (Figure 5). Flame the mouth of the tube and replace the cap. Flame your loop and let it cool.

4. Obtain a nutrient semisolid agar deep, and using your inoculating *needle*, repeat steps 2a–2d. Inoculate the semisolid agar deep by plunging the needle straight down the middle of the deep and then pulling it out through the same stab, as shown in Figure 6. Flame the mouth of the tube and replace the cap. Flame your needle and let it cool.

5. Using the other broth culture, label one tube of each medium as described in step 1; inoculate a broth culture, agar slant, and semisolid agar deep, as described in steps 2, 3, and 4, using your inoculating loop and needle.

6. Label one tube of each medium with *Proteus vulgaris* as described in step 1. To transfer *Proteus*

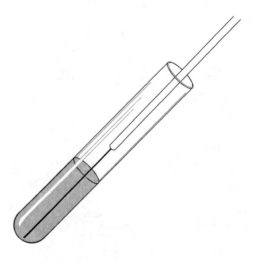

Figure 6

Inoculate an agar deep by stabbing into the agar with a needle.

vulgaris, flame your loop and allow it to cool. Flame the mouth of the tube, and use your inoculating loop to carefully scrape a small amount of the culture off of the agar. Do not gouge the agar. Flame the mouth of the tube and replace the cap. Inoculate a broth and a slant as described in steps 2 and 3. Inoculate a semisolid agar deep with an inoculating needle. Carefully scrape a small amount of

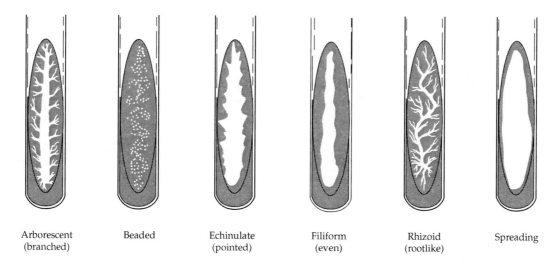

| Arborescent (branched) | Beaded | Echinulate (pointed) | Filiform (even) | Rhizoid (rootlike) | Spreading |

Figure 7

Patterns of growth on agar slants.

culture from the slant and inoculate the deep as described in step 4.

7. Incubate all tubes at 35°C until the next period.

8. Record the appearance of each culture, referring to Figure 7.

9. Make a smear of the *Lactococcus* broth culture and the *Lactococcus* slant culture. Perform a gram stain on both smears and compare them.

LABORATORY REPORT

Transfer of Bacteria: Aseptic Technique

NAME _____

DATE _____

LAB SECTION _____

Purpose _____

_____

_____

Data

Nutrient Broth

Describe the nutrient broth cultures.

Bacterium	Is it turbid?	Is flocculent, pellicle, or sediment present?	Pigment
Lactococcus lactis			
Pseudomonas aeruginosa			
Proteus vulgaris			

Nutrient Agar Slant

Sketch the appearance of each culture. Note any pigmentation.

Bacteria: Lactococcus lactis   Pseudomonas aeruginosa   Proteus vulgaris

Pattern of growth: _____   _____   _____

Nutrient Semisolid Agar Deep

Show the location of bacterial growth and note any pigment formation.

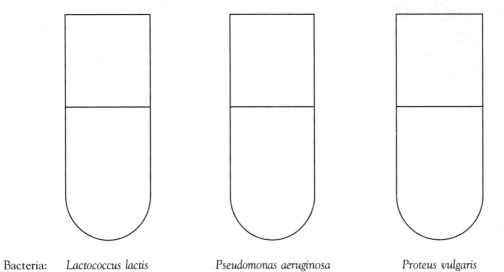

Bacteria: *Lactococcus lactis*   *Pseudomonas aeruginosa*   *Proteus vulgaris*

Comparison of Broth and Slant Cultures

	Lactococcus lactis	
	Broth Culture	Slant Culture
Gram stain		
Morphology		
Arrangement		

Questions

1. Did growth occur at different levels in the agar deep? _____

   _____

   _____

2. Were any of the bacteria growing in the semisolid agar deeps motile? _____ Explain.

   _____

   _____

   _____

3. What other methods can be used to determine motility? _____

_____

4. What is the primary use of slants? _____

Of deeps? _____

Of broths? _____

5. Can you determine whether a broth culture is pure (all one species) by visually inspecting it without a micro-

scope? _____ An agar deep culture? _____

An agar slant culture? _____

6. When is a loop preferable for transferring bacteria? Use an illustration from your results to answer. When is a

needle preferable? _____

_____

_____

7. What is the purpose of flaming the loop before use? After use? _____

_____

_____

8. Why must the loop be cool before touching it to a culture? Should you set it down to let it cool? How do you

determine when it is cool? _____

_____

_____

9. Why is aseptic technique important? _____

_____

_____

Critical Thinking

1. Why was the arrangement of *Lactococcus* from the broth culture different than that from the slant culture in the second period?

2. What evolutionary advantage would there be to the formation of a pellicle in a liquid medium by a bacterium?

3. How can you tell that the media provided for this exercise were sterile?

Isolation of Bacteria by Dilution Techniques

Experience is the father of wisdom, and memory the mother.

Thomas Fuller

Objectives

After completing this exercise, you should be able to:

1. Isolate bacteria by using the streak plate and pour plate techniques.
2. Prepare and maintain a pure culture.

Background

In nature most microbes are found growing in environments that contain many different organisms. Unfortunately, mixed cultures are of little use in studying microorganisms because of the difficulty they present in determining which organism is responsible for any observed activity. A **pure culture,** one containing a single kind of microbe, is required in order to study concepts such as growth characteristics, pathogenicity, metabolism, and antibiotic susceptibility. Because bacteria are too small to separate directly without sophisticated micromanipulation equipment, indirect methods of separation must be used.

In the 1870s, Joseph Lister attempted to obtain pure cultures by performing serial dilutions until each of his containers theoretically contained one bacterium. However, success was very limited, and **contamination,** the presence of unwanted microorganisms, was common. In 1880, Robert Koch prepared solid media, after which microbiologists could separate bacteria by dilution and trap them on the solid media. An isolated bacterium grows into a visible colony that consists of one kind of bacterium.

Currently there are three dilution methods commonly used for the isolation of bacteria: the streak plate, the spread plate, and the pour plate. In the **streak plate technique,** a loop is used to streak the mixed sample many times over the surface of a solid culture medium in a Petri plate. Theoretically, the process of streaking the loop repeatedly over the agar surface causes the bacteria to fall off the loop one by one and ultimately to be distributed over the agar surface, where each cell develops into a colony. The streak plate is the most common isolation technique in use today.

The spread plate and pour plate are quantitative techniques that allow determination of the number of bacteria in a sample. In the **spread plate technique,** a small amount of a previously diluted specimen is spread over the surface of a solid medium using a spreading rod.

In the **pour plate technique,** a small amount of diluted sample is mixed with melted agar and poured into empty, sterile Petri dishes. After incubation, bacterial growth is visible as colonies in and on the agar of a pour plate. To determine the number of bacteria in the original sample, a plate with between 25 and 250 colonies is selected. Fewer than 25 colonies is inaccurate because a single contaminant causes at least a 4% error. A plate with greater than 250 colonies is difficult to count. The number of bacteria in the original sample is calculated using the following equation:

$$\frac{\text{Colony-forming units}}{\text{per ml}} = \frac{\text{Number of colonies}}{\text{Dilution*} \times \text{Amount plated}}$$

Materials

Petri plates containing nutrient agar (2)

Tubes containing melted nutrient agar (3)

Sterile Petri dishes (3)

250-ml beaker

Sterile 1-ml pipettes (3)

Propipette or pipette bulb

Nutrient agar slant (second period)

---

*In this exercise, 1 ml of sample is put into each plate. Dilution refers to the dilution of the sample. For example, if 37 colonies were present on the 1:8000 plate, the calculation would be as follows:

Colony-forming units per ml =
$$\frac{37}{1:8000 \times 1} = 37 \times 8000 = 296{,}000 = 2.96 \times 10^5$$

Cultures

Mixed broth culture of bacteria

Turbid nutrient broth

Techniques Required

Compound light microscopy

Aseptic technique

Pipetting

Serial dilution techniques

Procedure

Streak Plate

1. Label the bottoms of two nutrient agar plates to correspond to the two broth cultures: mixed culture and turbid broth.
2. Flame the inoculating loop to redness, allow it to cool, and aseptically obtain a loopful of one broth culture.
3. The streaking procedure may be done with the Petri plate on the table (Figure 1a) or held in your hand (Figure 1b).
   a. To streak a plate (Figure 2), lift one edge of the Petri plate cover, and streak the first sector by making as many streaks as possible without overlapping previous streaks. Do not gouge the agar while streaking the plate. Hold the loop as you would hold a pencil or paintbrush, and gently touch the surface of the agar.
   b. Flame your loop and let it cool. Turn the plate so the next sector is on top. Streak through one area of the first sector, and then streak a few times away from the first sector.
   c. Flame your loop, turn the plate again, and streak through one area of the second sector. Then streak the third sector.
   d. Flame your loop, streak through one area of the third sector, and then streak the remaining area of the agar surface, being careful not to make additional contact with any streaks in the previous sections. Flame your loop before setting it down. Why? _____

   _____

4. Streak two plates: one of the mixed culture provided and one of the turbid broth from an environmental sample. Label each plate on the bottom with your name and lab section, the date, and the source of the inoculum.
5. Incubate the plates in an inverted position in the 35°C incubator (or at room temperature, depending

on the inoculum) until discrete, isolated colonies develop (usually 24 to 48 hours). Why inverted?

_____

6. After incubation, record your results. Use proper terms to describe the colonies.
7. Prepare a subculture of one colony. Sterilize your needle by flaming it. Let it cool. Why use a needle instead of a loop? _____
   To subculture, touch the center of a small isolated colony located on a streak line, and then aseptically streak a sterile nutrient agar slant. How can you tell whether you touched only one colony and whether you have a pure culture? _____

   _____

8. Incubate the slant at 35°C until good growth is observed. Describe the growth pattern.

Pour Plate (Figure 3)

1. Label the bottoms of three empty, sterile Petri dishes with your name and lab section and the date. Label one dish "1:20," another "1:400," and the third one "1:8000." Place the labeled dishes on your workbench right-side up.
2. Fill a beaker with hot (45–50°C) water (about 3–6 cm deep), and place three tubes of melted nutrient agar in the beaker. Each tube contains 19 ml of nutrient agar.
3. Select a mixed broth culture.
4. Remove a pipette, attach a bulb, and aseptically transfer 1 ml of the broth to a tube of melted agar. Mix well, as shown in Figure 4. Using a different pipette, transfer 1 ml from this tube to a second tube. Work quickly so the agar does not solidify in the pipette. Aseptically pour the contents of the first tube into Petri dish 1:20. Discard the pipettes in the container of disinfectant.
5. Mix the second tube. With the third pipette, aseptically transfer 1 ml to the third tube. Pour the contents of the second tube into dish 1:400. Mix the third tube and pour its contents into the remaining dish, 1:8000.
6. Discard the tubes properly. Let the agar harden in the plates, and then incubate them at 35°C in an inverted position until growth is seen. *Suggestion:* When incubating multiple plates, use a rubber band to hold them together.
7. After incubation, count the number of colonies on the plates. Remember that more than 250 is too numerous to count, and less than 25 is too few to count.

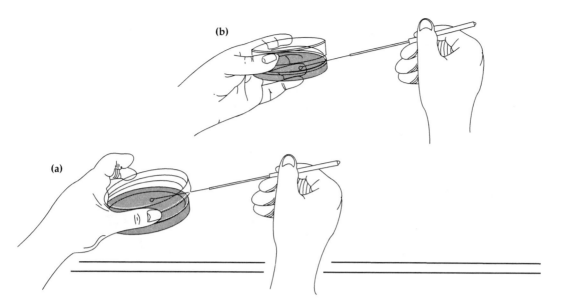

Figure 1

Inoculation of a solid medium in a Petri plate. Lift one edge of the cover while the plate **(a)** rests on the table or **(b)** is held.

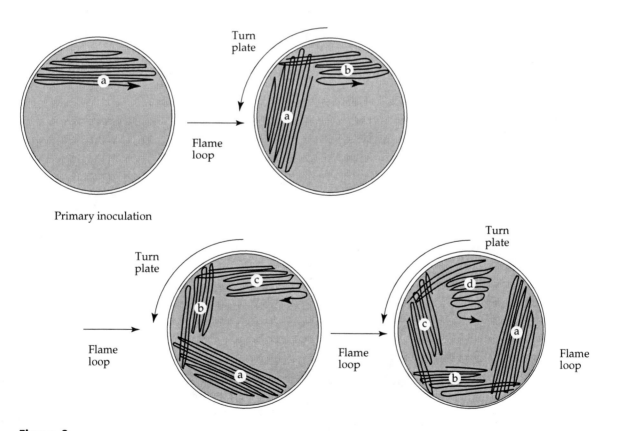

Figure 2

Streak plate technique for pure culture isolation of bacteria. The direction of streaking is indicated by the arrows. Between each section, sterilize the loop and reinoculate with a fraction of the bacteria by going back across the previous section.

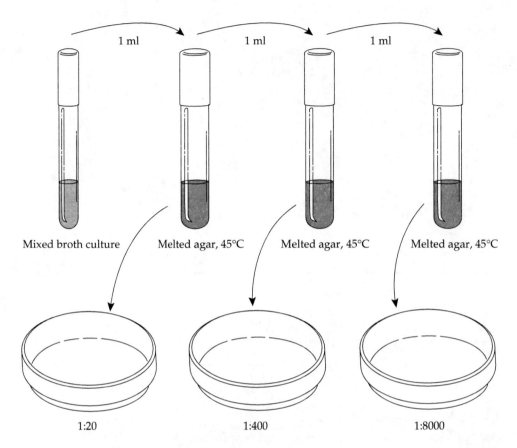

1 ml   1 ml   1 ml

Mixed broth culture   Melted agar, 45°C   Melted agar, 45°C   Melted agar, 45°C

1:20   1:400   1:8000

Figure 3

Pour plate technique. Bacteria are diluted through a series of tubes containing 19 ml
of melted nutrient agar. The agar and bacteria are poured into sterile Petri dishes.
The bacteria will form colonies where they are trapped in the agar.

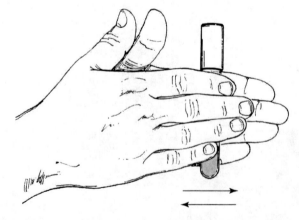

Figure 4

Mix the inoculum in a tube of melted agar by rolling the tube
between your hands.

LABORATORY REPORT

Isolation of Bacteria by Dilution Techniques

NAME _____

DATE _____

LAB SECTION _____

Purpose _____

_____

_____

Data

Streak Plate

Sketch the appearance of the streak plates.

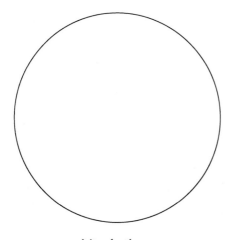

Mixed culture

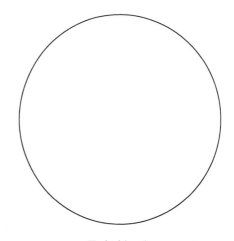

Turbid broth

Fill in the following table using colonies from the most isolated streak areas.

Culture	Colony Description (Each different-appearing colony should be described.)				
	Diameter	Appearance	Margin	Elevation	Color
Mixed culture					
Turbid broth					

Pour Plate

Dilution	Number of Colonies
1:20	
1:400	
1:8000	

Calculate the number of colony-forming units per milliliter in the mixed culture. Which plate will you use for your calculations? _____
Show your calculations.

_____ Colony-forming units per ml

Subculture

Describe the growth on your slant. _____

Do you appear to have a pure culture? _____

Questions

1. How many different bacteria were in the mixed culture? _____ How many in the

    turbid broth? _____ How can you tell? _____

    _____

2. How do the colonies on the surface of the pour plate differ from those suspended in the agar?

    _____

    _____

3. What is a contaminant? _____

4. How would you determine whether a colony was a contaminant on a streak plate? _____

    _____

    On a pour plate? _____

    _____

5. What would happen if the plates were incubated a week longer? _____

    A month? _____

6. How could your streak plate technique be improved? _____

    _____

    _____

Critical Thinking

1. Could some bacteria grow on the streak plate and not be seen using the pour plate technique? Explain.

2. What is a disadvantage of the streak plate technique? Of the pour plate technique?

3. Will the isolated colonies always be in the fourth sector on the streak plate?

Special Media for Isolating Bacteria

Objectives

After completing this exercise, you should be able to:

1. Differentiate between selective and differential media.
2. Provide an application for enrichment and selective media.

Background

One of the major limitations of dilution techniques used to isolate bacteria is that organisms present in limited amounts may be diluted out on plates filled with dominant bacteria. For example, if the culture to be isolated has 1 million of bacterium A and only 1 of bacterium B, bacterium B will probably be limited to the first sector in a streak plate. To help isolate organisms found in the minority, various enrichment and selective culturing methods are available that either enhance the growth of some organisms or inhibit the growth of other organisms. **Selective media** contain chemicals that prevent the growth of unwanted bacteria without inhibiting the growth of the desired organism. **Enrichment media,** which are usually liquid media, contain

chemicals that enhance the growth of desired bacteria. Other bacteria will grow, but the growth of the desired bacteria will be increased.

Another category of media useful in identifying bacteria is **differential media.** These media contain various nutrients that allow the investigator to distinguish one bacterium from another by how they metabolize or change the media with a waste product.

Because multiple methods and multiple media exist, you must be able to match the correct procedure to the desired microbe. For example, if bacterium B is salt-tolerant, a high concentration (>5%) of salt could be added to the culture medium. Physical conditions can also be used to select for a bacterium. If bacterium B is heat-resistant, the specimen could be heated before isolation. Dyes such as phenol red, eosin, or methylene blue are sometimes included in differential media. Products of bacterial metabolism can react with these dyes to produce a color change in the medium. You will study bacterial metabolism in the exercises in Part 4. The dyes (eosin and methylene blue) in eosin methylene blue (EMB) agar are also selective. These dyes inhibit the growth of some bacteria. Three culture media will be compared in this exercise (Table 1).

Table 1

Major Chemical Components of Media Used in This Exercise

	Nutrient Agar	Mannitol Salt Agar	EMB Agar
Peptone	0.5%	1.0%	1.0%
NaCl	0.8%	7.5%	
Agar	1.5%	1.5%	1.5%
Mannitol		1.0%	
Lactose, sucrose			0.5% each
Eosin			0.04%
Methylene blue			0.0065%
Phenol red		0.025%	

Materials

Petri plates containing nutrient agar (2)

Petri plates containing mannitol salt agar (2)

Petri plates containing EMB agar (2)

Gram-staining reagents

Cultures

Escherichia coli

Micrococcus luteus

Pseudomonas aeruginosa

Staphylococcus epidermidis

Unknown mixed culture

Techniques Required

Compound light microscopy

Smear preparation

Gram staining

Aseptic technique

Inoculating loop technique

Streak plate procedure

Procedure

1. Using a marker, divide one nutrient agar plate into four sections by labeling the bottom. Repeat to mark one mannitol salt plate and one EMB plate. Label one quadrant on each plate for each culture.

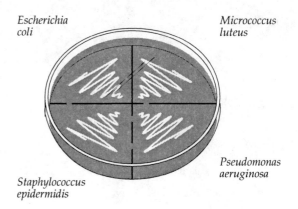

Figure 1

Divide a Petri plate into four sections by drawing lines on the bottom of the plate. Inoculate each section by streaking it with an inoculating loop.

2. Streak each culture on the agar, as shown in Figure 1.
3. Label the remaining nutrient agar, mannitol salt, and EMB plates with the number of your unknown. The unknown contains two different bacteria.
4. Streak your "unknown" onto the appropriate plates using the streaking technique.
5. Incubate the plates in an inverted position at 35°C. Record the results after 24–48 hours.
6. Perform a Gram stain on one colony of each different organism. Why don't you have to perform a Gram stain on each organism from every medium?

Special Media for Isolating Bacteria

NAME _____

DATE _____

LAB SECTION _____

Purpose _____

_____

_____

Data

Organism	Nutrient Agar Growth: +/–	Nutrient Agar Appearance	Mannitol Salt Agar Growth: +/–	Mannitol Salt Agar Appearance	EMB Agar Growth: +/–	EMB Agar Appearance	Gram-Stain Results
E. coli							
M. luteus							
P. aeruginosa							
S. epidermidis							
Unknown							

Questions

1. What two organisms are in your mixed culture? _____

   Could you identify them from the Gram stain? _____

   How did you identify them? _____

   _____

2. How did the results observed on the mannitol salt and EMB correlate to the Gram reaction of the bacteria?

   _____

   _____

3. Which medium is selective? _____

4. What is the purpose of peptone in the media? _____

_____

Of agar in the media? _____

_____

Critical Thinking

1. What ingredient makes mannitol salt selective? _____

2. Fill in the blanks in this diagram to make a key to these bacteria: *Escherichia coli, Micrococcus luteus, Pseudomonas aeruginosa, Staphylococcus epidermidis*.

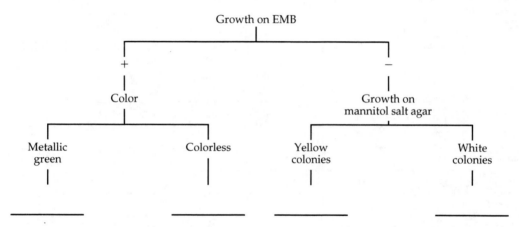

Circle or highlight the gram-positive bacteria in one color; use a different color to circle or highlight the gram-negative bacteria.

3. Design an enrichment medium to isolate a detergent-degrading bacterium that is found in soil.

Carbohydrate Catabolism

The men who try to do something and fail are infinitely better than those who try nothing and succeed.

LLOYD JONES

Objectives

After completing this exercise, you should be able to:

1. Define the following terms: carbohydrate, catabolism, and hydrolytic enzymes.
2. Differentiate between oxidative and fermentative catabolism.
3. Perform and interpret microbial starch hydrolysis and OF tests.

Background

Chemical reactions that release energy from the decomposition of complex organic molecules are referred to as **catabolism.** Most bacteria catabolize carbohydrates for carbon and energy. **Carbohydrates** are organic molecules that contain carbon, hydrogen, and oxygen in the ratio $(CH_2O)_n$. Carbohydrates can be classified based on size: monosaccharides, oligosaccharides, and polysaccharides. **Monosaccharides** are simple sugars containing from three to seven carbon atoms. **Oligosaccharides** are composed of two to about 20 monosaccharide molecules; *disaccharides* are the most common oligosaccharides. **Polysaccharides** consist of eight or more monosaccharide molecules.

Exoenzymes are mainly **hydrolytic enzymes** that leave the cell and break down, by the addition of water, large substrates into smaller components, which can then be transported into the cell. Amylase hydrolyzes the polysaccharide starch into smaller carbohydrates. Glucose, a monosaccharide, can be released by hydrolysis (Figure 1). In the laboratory, the presence of an exoenzyme is determined by looking for a change in the substrate outside of a bacterial colony.

Glucose can enter a cell and be catabolized; some bacteria, using endoenzymes, catabolize glucose oxidatively, producing carbon dioxide and water. **Oxidative catabolism** requires the presence of molecular oxygen (O_2). Most bacteria, however, can ferment glucose without using oxygen. **Fermentative catabolism** does not require oxygen but may occur in its presence. The metabolic end-products of fermentation are small organic molecules, usually organic acids. Some bacteria produce gases from the fermentation of carbohydrates.

Whether an organism is oxidative or fermentative can be determined by using Rudolph Hugh and Einar Leifson's OF basal media with the desired carbohydrate added. **OF medium** is a nutrient semisolid agar deep containing a *high* concentration of carbohydrate and a *low* concentration of peptone. The peptone will support the growth bacteria that don't use the carbohydrate. Two tubes are used: one open to the air and one sealed to keep air out. OF medium contains the indicator bromthymol blue, which turns yellow in the presence of acids, indicating catabolism of the carbohydrate. Alkaline conditions, due to the use of peptone and not the carbohydrate, are indicated by a dark blue color due to ammonia production. If the carbohydrate is metabolized in both tubes, fermentation has occurred. An organism that can only use the carbohydrate under aerobic conditions will produce acid in the open tube only. Acids are produced as intermediates in respiration, and the indicator will turn yellow in the top of the open tube. This organism is called "oxidative" in an OF test.

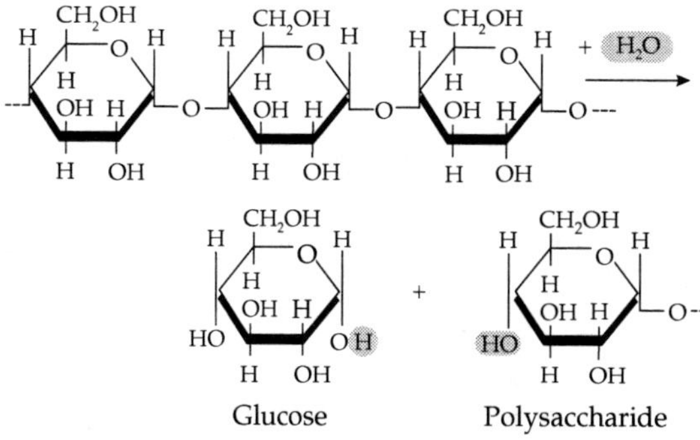

Figure 1

Starch hydrolysis. A molecule of water is used when starch is hydrolyzed.

From *Laboratory Experiments in Microbiology,* Eighth Edition, Ted R. Johnson and Christine L. Case. Copyright © 2006 by Pearson Education, Inc. Published by Benjamin Cummings, Inc. All rights reserved.

Carbohydrate catabolism will be demonstrated in this exercise. These differential tests will be important in identifying bacteria in later exercises.

Materials

Petri plate containing nutrient starch agar

OF-glucose deeps (2)

Mineral oil

Second Period

Gram's iodine

OF-glucose deep

Cultures (as assigned)

Bacillus subtilis

Escherichia coli

Pseudomonas aeruginosa

Alcaligenes faecalis

Techniques Required

Inoculating loop and needle technique

Aseptic technique

Procedure

Starch Hydrolysis

1. With a marker, divide the starch agar into three sectors by labeling the bottom of the plate.
2. Using a loop, streak a short single line of *Bacillus, Escherichia,* and *Pseudomonas*.
3. Incubate the plate, inverted, at 35°C for 24 hours. After growth occurs, the plate may be refrigerated at 5°C until the next lab period.
4. Record any bacterial growth, and then flood the plate with Gram's iodine (Figure 2). Areas of starch

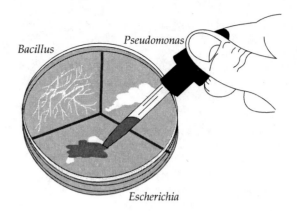

Figure 2

Starch hydrolysis test. After incubation, add iodine to the plate to detect the presence of starch.

hydrolysis will appear clear, while unchanged starch will stain dark blue. Record your results.

OF-Glucose

1. Using an inoculating needle, inoculate two tubes of OF-glucose media with the assigned bacterial culture (*Escherichia, Pseudomonas,* or *Alcaligenes*).
2. Pour about 5 mm of mineral oil over the medium in one of the tubes. Replace the cap.
3. Incubate both tubes at 35°C until the next lab period.
4. Compare the inoculated tubes and an uninoculated OF-glucose tube. Record the following: the presence of growth, whether glucose was used, and the type of metabolism. Motility can also be ascertained from the OF tubes. How? _____

_____

5. Observe and record the results from the microorganisms you did not culture.

Carbohydrate Catabolism

NAME _____

DATE _____

LAB SECTION _____

Purpose _____

_____

_____

Data

Record your results in the following tables.

Starch Hydrolysis

Organism	Growth	Color of Medium Around Colonies After Addition of Iodine	Starch Hydrolysis: (+) = yes (−) = no
Bacillus subtilis			
Pseudomonas aeruginosa			
Escherichia coli			

OF-Glucose

Color of uninoculated medium: _____

Organism	Growth		Color		Fermenter (F), Oxidative (O), Neither (−)	Motile
	Aerobic Tube	Anaerobic Tube	Aerobic Tube	Anaerobic Tube		
Pseudomonas aeruginosa						
Alcaligenes faecalis						
Escherichia coli						

Questions

1. Which organism(s) gave a positive test for starch hydrolysis? _____

    _____

    How can you tell? _____

2. What would be found in the clear area that would not be found in the blue area of a starch agar plate after the

    addition of iodine? _____

    _____

3. How can you tell amylase is an exoenzyme and not an endoenzyme? _____

    _____

4. How can you tell from OF-glucose medium whether an organism uses glucose aerobically? _____

    _____

    Ferments glucose? _____

    Doesn't use glucose? _____

5. If an organism grows in the OF-glucose medium that is exposed to air, is the organism oxidative or fermenta-

    tive? Explain. _____

    _____

6. Why is it important to first determine whether growth occurred in a differential medium, such as starch agar,

    before examining the plate for starch hydrolysis? _____

    _____

    _____

Critical Thinking

1. Aerobic organisms degrade glucose, producing carbon dioxide and water. What acid turns the indicator yellow?

2. How can organisms that don't use starch grow on a starch agar plate?

3. If iodine were not available, how would you determine whether starch hydrolysis had occurred?

4. Locate the H^+ and OH^- ions from the water molecule that was split (hydrolyzed) in this reaction, showing esculin hydrolysis.

Esculin   Glucose   +   Esculetin

Fermentation

Objectives

After completing this exercise, you should be able to:

1. Define fermentation.
2. Perform and interpret carbohydrate fermentation tests.
3. Perform and interpret the MR and V–P tests.
4. Perform and interpret the citrate test.

Background

Once a bacterium has been determined to be fermentative by the OF test, further tests can determine which carbohydrates, in addition to glucose, are fermented; in some instances, the end-products can also be determined. Many carbohydrates—including monosaccharides such as glucose, disaccharides like sucrose, and polysaccharides such as starch—can be fermented. Many bacteria produce organic acids (for example, lactic acid) and hydrogen and carbon dioxide gases from carbohydrate fermentation (Figure 1). A **fermentation tube** is used to detect acid and gas production from carbohydrates. The fermentation medium contains peptone, an acid–base indicator (phenol red), an inverted tube to trap gas, and 0.5–1.0% of the desired carbohydrate. In Figure 2, the phenol red indicator is red (neutral) in an uninoculated fermentation tube; fermentation that results in acid production will turn the indicator yellow (pH of 6.8 or below). When gas is produced during fermentation, some will be trapped in the inverted, or Durham, tube. Fermentation occurs with or without oxygen present; however, during prolonged incubation periods (greater than 24 hours), many bacteria will begin growing oxidatively on the peptone after exhausting the carbohydrate supplied,

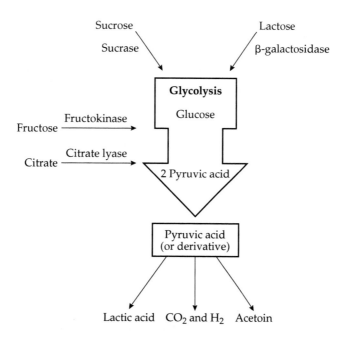

Figure 1

Fermentation. Bacteria are often identified by their enzymes. These enzymes can be detected by observing a bacterium's ability to grow on specific compounds. For example, *E. coli* and *Salmonella* are distinguished because *E. coli* can ferment lactose, and typical *Salmonella* cannot.

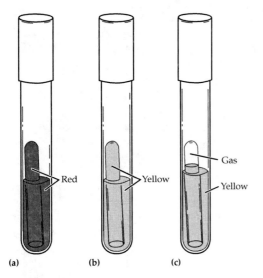

Figure 2

Carbohydrate fermentation tube. **(a)** The phenol red indicator is red in a neutral or alkaline solution. **(b)** Phenol red turns yellow in the presence of acids. **(c)** Gases are trapped in the inverted tube while the indicator shows the production of acid.

Table 1

Simmons Citrate Agar

Ingredient	Amount
Sodium citrate	0.2%
Sodium chloride	0.5%
Monoammonium phosphate	0.1%
Dipotassium phosphate	0.1%
Magnesium sulfate	0.02%
Agar	1.5%
Bromthymol blue	0.0008%

causing neutralization of the indicator and turning it red due to ammonia production.

Fermentation processes can produce a variety of end-products, depending on the substrate, the incubation, and the organism. In some instances, large amounts of acid may be produced, while in others, a majority of neutral products may result (Figure 3a). The **MRVP test** is used to distinguish between organisms that produce large amounts of acid from glucose and those that produce the neutral product *acetoin*. MRVP medium is a glucose-supplemented nutrient broth used for the **methyl red (MR) test** and the **Voges–Proskauer (V–P) test.** If an organism produces a large amount of organic acid from glucose, the medium will remain red when methyl red is added in a positive MR test, indicating that the pH is below 4.4. If neutral products are produced, methyl red will turn yellow, indicating a pH above 6.0. The production of acetoin is detected by the addition of potassium hydroxide and α-naphthol. If acetoin is present, the upper part of the medium will turn red; a negative V–P test will turn the medium light brown. The chemical process is shown in Figure 3b. The production of acetoin is dependent on the length of incubation, as shown in Figure 4.

The ability of some bacteria to ferment citrate can be useful for identifying bacteria. When citric acid or sodium citrate is in solution, it loses a proton or Na^+ to form a citrate ion. Bacteria with the enzyme citrate lyase can break down citrate to form pyruvate, which can be reduced in fermentation. Simmons citrate agar (Table 1) contains citrate as the only carbon source and ammonium (NH_4^+) as the only nitrogen source. When bacteria use citrate and ammonium, the medium is alkalized because of ammonia (NH_3) produced from NH_4^+. The indicator bromthymol blue changes to blue when the medium is alkalized, indicating a positive citrate utilization test.

Materials

Glucose fermentation tube

Lactose fermentation tube

Sucrose fermentation tube

MRVP broths (4)

Simmons citrate agar slants (2)

Second Period

MRVP broth

Glucose fermentation tube

Simmons citrate agar slant

Parafilm squares

Empty test tube

Methyl red

V–P reagent I, α-naphthol solution

V–P reagent II, potassium hydroxide (40%)

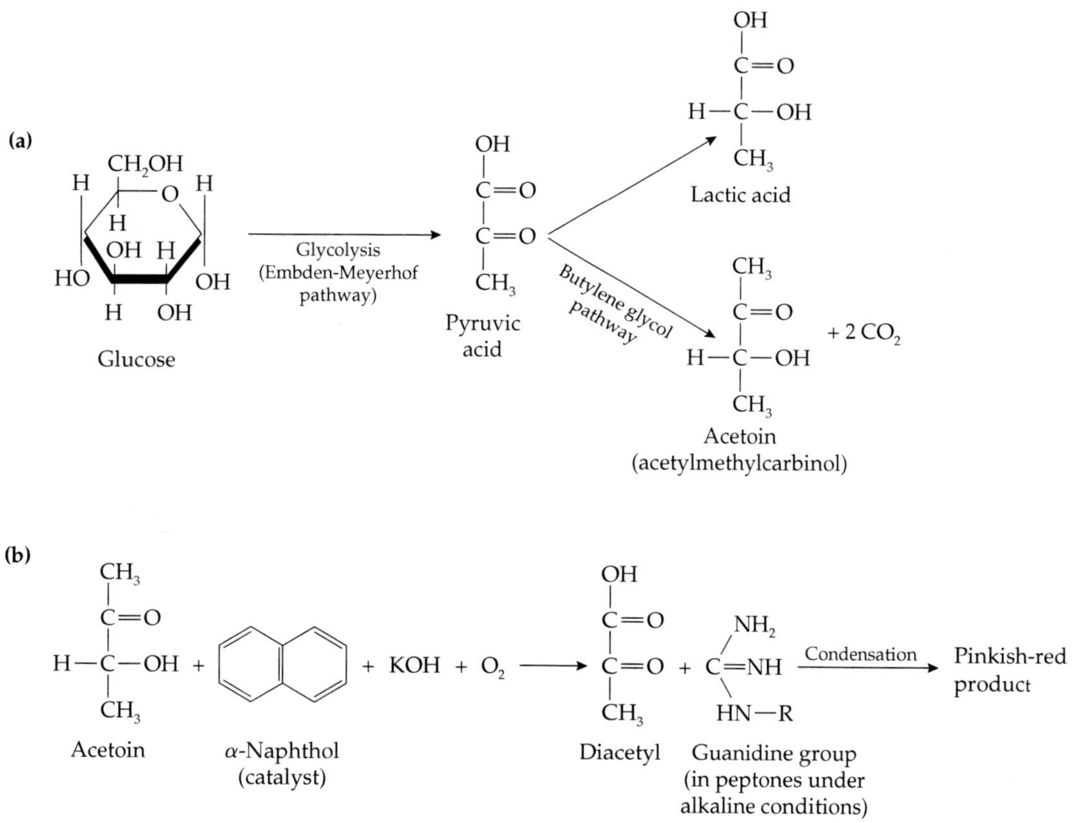

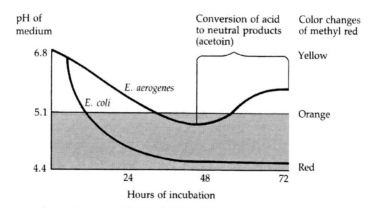

Figure 3

MRVP test. **(a)** Organic acids, such as lactic acid, or neutral products, such as
acetoin, may result from fermentation. **(b)** Potassium hydroxide (KOH) and
α-naphthol are used to detect acetoin.

Figure 4

The production of acetoin is dependent on incubation time and pH.

Cultures (as assigned)

Escherichia coli

Enterobacter aerogenes

Alcaligenes faecalis

Proteus vulgaris

Techniques Required

Inoculating loop technique

Aseptic technique

OF test

Procedure

Fermentation Tubes

1. Use a loop to inoculate the fermentation tubes with the assigned bacterial culture.
2. Incubate the tubes at 35°C. Examine them at 24 and 48 hours for growth, acid, and gas production. Compare them to an uninoculated fermentation tube. Why is it important to record the presence of growth? _____
   _____
3. Record your results with this culture, as well as your results for the other species tested.

MRVP Tests

1. Using a loop, inoculate two MRVP tubes with *Escherichia* and two with *Enterobacter*.

2. Incubate the tubes at 35°C for 48 hours or longer. Why is time of incubation important (Figure 4)?
   _____
   _____

3. To one tube of each set (*Escherichia* and *Enterobacter*), add 5 drops of methyl red. Record the resulting color. Red indicates a positive methyl red test (Figure 3a).
4. To the other set of two tubes, add 0.6 ml (12 drops) of V–P reagent I and 0.2 ml (2 or 3 drops) of V–P reagent II.
5. Cover each tube with a Parafilm square, and shake the tubes carefully. Discard the Parafilm in the disinfectant jar.
6. Leave the caps off to expose the media to oxygen in order to oxidize the acetoin (Figure 3b). Allow the tubes to stand for 15 to 30 minutes. A positive V–P test will develop a pinkish-red color.
7. Create controls. Pour half of the contents of an uninoculated MRVP broth into an empty test tube. Perform the MR test (step 3) on one tube. Perform the V–P test (steps 4–6) on the other tube.
8. Record your results.

Citrate Test

1. Using a loop, inoculate one citrate slant with *Escherichia coli* and the other slant with *Enterobacter aerogenes*.
2. Incubate the tubes at 35°C until the next lab period.
3. Compare the tubes to an uninoculated citrate slant and record your results.

Fermentation

NAME _____

DATE _____

LAB SECTION _____

Purpose _____
_____
_____

Data

Fermentation Tubes

Color of uninoculated medium: _____

Organism		Carbohydrate											
		Glucose				Lactose				Sucrose			
		Growth	Color	Acid	Gas	Growth	Color	Acid	Gas	Growth	Color	Acid	Gas
Escherichia coli	24 hr												
	48 hr												
Enterobacter aerogenes	24 hr												
	48 hr												
Alcaligenes faecalis	24 hr												
	48 hr												
Proteus vulgaris	24 hr												
	48 hr												

108   Fermentation

MRVP Tests

Organism	Growth	MR		V–P	
		Color	+ or −	Color	+ or −
Escherichia coli					
Enterobacter aerogenes					
Controls					

Citrate Test

Organism	Growth	Color	+ or −
Escherichia coli			
Enterobacter aerogenes			
Controls			

Questions

1. Why are fermentation tubes evaluated at 24 and 48 hours? _____

   _____

   What would happen if an organism used up all the carbohydrate in a fermentation tube? _____

   _____

   What would the organism use for energy? _____ What color would the indicator be then?

   _____

2. If an organism metabolizes glucose aerobically, what result will occur in the fermentation tubes?

   _____

   _____

3. Were these media differential or selective? _____

   _____

Critical Thinking

1. Could an organism be both MR and V–P positive? Explain.

2. Could an organism be a fermenter and also be both MR and V–P negative? Explain.

3. How could you determine whether a bacterium fermented the following carbohydrates: mannitol, sorbitol, adonitol, or arabinose?

4. If a bacterium cannot ferment glucose, why not test its ability to ferment other carbohydrates?

Protein Catabolism, Part 1

Objectives

After completing this exercise, you should be able to:

1. Determine a bacterium's ability to hydrolyze gelatin.
2. Test for the presence of urease.

Background

Proteins are large organic molecules that include cellular enzymes and many structures. The subunits that make up a protein are called **amino acids** (Figure 1). Amino acids consist of carbon, hydrogen, oxygen, nitrogen, and sometimes, sulfur. Amino acids bond together by **peptide bonds** (Figure 2), forming a small chain (a **peptide**) or a larger molecule (a **polypeptide**).

Bacteria can hydrolyze the peptides or polypeptides to release amino acids (Figure 2). They use the amino acids as carbon and energy sources when carbohydrates are not available. However, amino acids are primarily used in anabolic reactions.

Large protein molecules, such as gelatin, are hydrolyzed by exoenzymes, and the smaller products of hydrolysis are transported into the cell. Hydrolysis of gelatin can be demonstrated by growing bacteria in nutrient gelatin. Nutrient gelatin dissolves in warm water (50°C), solidifies (**gels**) when cooled below 25°C, and liquefies (**sols**) when heated to about 25°C. When

an exoenzyme hydrolyzes gelatin, it liquefies and does not solidify even when cooled below 20°C.

Urea is a waste product of protein digestion in most vertebrates and is excreted in the urine. Presence of the enzyme **urease,** which liberates ammonia from urea (Figure 3), is a useful diagnostic test for identifying bacteria. **Urea agar** contains peptone, glucose, urea, and phenol red. The pH of the prepared medium is 6.8 (phenol red turns yellow). During incubation, bacteria possessing urease will produce ammonia, which raises the pH of the medium, turning the indicator fuchsia (hot pink) at pH 8.4.

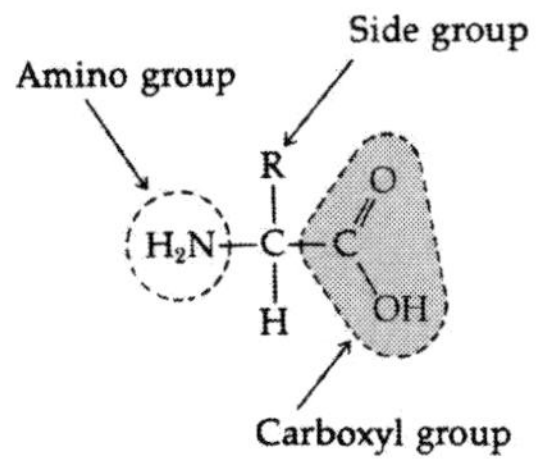

Figure 1

General structural formula for an amino acid. The letter R stands for any of a number of groups of atoms. Different amino acids have different R groups.

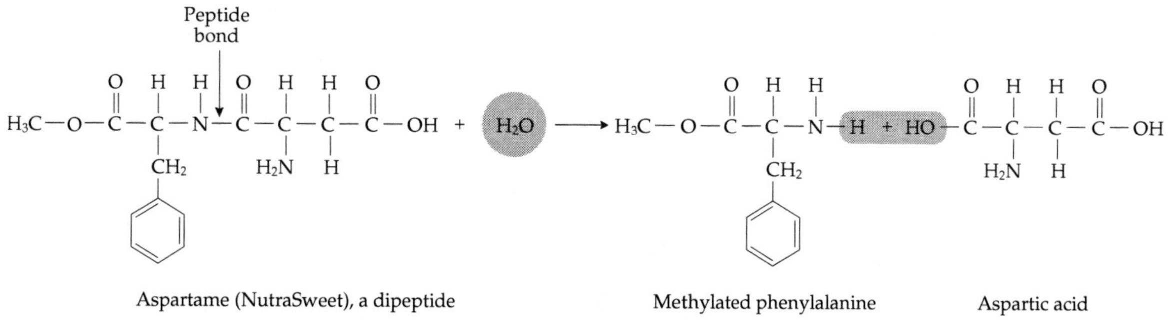

Figure 2

Hydrolysis of peptides. A molecule of water is used when the peptide is hydrolyzed.

From *Laboratory Experiments in Microbiology,* Eighth Edition, Ted R. Johnson and Christine L. Case. Copyright © 2006 by Pearson Education, Inc. Published by Benjamin Cummings, Inc. All rights reserved.

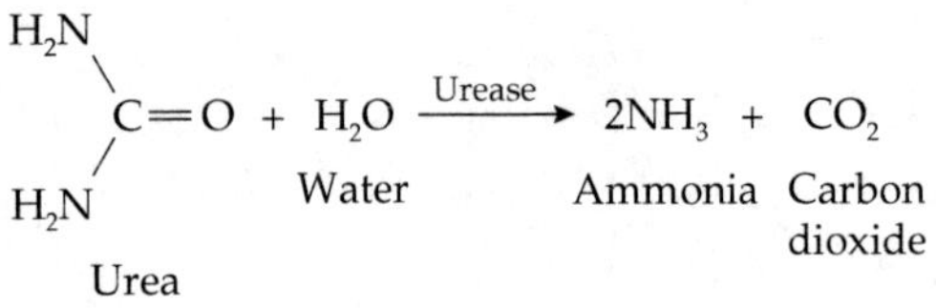

$$\begin{array}{c} H_2N \\ \diagdown \\ C{=}O \ + \ H_2O \ \xrightarrow{\ \text{Urease}\ } \ 2NH_3 \ + \ CO_2 \\ \diagup \\ H_2N \end{array}$$

Urea   Water   Ammonia   Carbon dioxide

Figure 3

Urea hydrolysis.

Materials

Tubes containing nutrient gelatin (2)

Tubes containing urea agar (2)

Cultures

Pseudomonas aeruginosa

Proteus vulgaris

Techniques Required

Inoculating loop technique

Aseptic technique

Procedure

1. Label one tube of each medium "*Pseudomonas*" and the other tube "*Proteus*."
2. Perform the gelatin hydrolysis. Examine the nutrient gelatin: Is it solid or liquid? _____
   What is the temperature of the laboratory? _____
   If the gelatin is solid, what would you need to do to liquefy it? _____
   To resolidify it? _____
   a. Inoculate one tube with *Pseudomonas* and one with *Proteus*, using your inoculating needle.
   b. Incubate the tubes at room temperature, and record your observations at 2 to 4 days and again at 4 to 7 days. Do not agitate the tube when the gelatin is liquid. Why? _____
   _____
   c. If the gelatin has liquefied, place the tube in a beaker of crushed ice for a few minutes. Is the gelatin still liquefied? _____
   Record your results. Indicate liquefaction or hydrolysis by (+).
3. Conduct a urease test.
   a. Inoculate one urea agar slant with *Pseudomonas* and one with *Proteus*.
   b. Incubate the tubes for 24 to 48 hours at 35°C. Record your results: (+) for the presence of urease (red) and (−) for no urease. What color is phenol red at pH 6.8 or below? _____
   At pH 8.4 or above? _____

LABORATORY REPORT

Protein Catabolism, Part 1

NAME _____

DATE _____

LAB SECTION _____

Purpose _____

_____

_____

Data

Fill in this table and the one on the next page.

Controls	Appearance of Uninoculated Tube
Gelatin	
Urea agar	

Diagram the appearance of the gelatin.

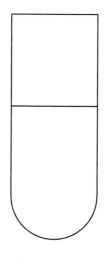

Pseudomonas aeruginosa

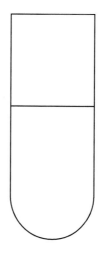

Proteus vulgaris

Test	Results	
	Pseudomonas aeruginosa	*Proteus vulgaris*
Gelatin hydrolysis at _____ days Growth		
Hydrolysis		
Urea agar Growth		
Hydrolysis		

Questions

1. Nutrient gelatin can be incubated at 35°C. What would have to be done to determine hydrolysis after incubation at 35°C? _____

   _____

   _____

2. What is the source of urea in the body? _____

   _____

   _____

Critical Thinking

1. Why is agar used as a solidifying agent in culture media instead of gelatin?

2. What would you find in the liquid of hydrolyzed gelatin?

3. When changing a baby's wet diapers, one smells ammonia. Why?

4. *Helicobacter pylori* bacteria grow in the human stomach. These bacteria produce a large amount of urease. Of what value is this urease to *Helicobacter*?

Protein Catabolism, Part 2

Objectives

After completing this exercise, you should be able to:

1. Define the following terms: deamination and decarboxylation.
2. Explain the derivation of H_2S in decomposition.
3. Perform and interpret an indole test.
4. Interpret results from MIO medium.

Background

Once amino acids are taken into a bacterial cell, various metabolic processes can occur using endoenzymes. Before an amino acid can be used as a carbon and energy source, the amino group must be removed. The removal of an amino group is called **deamination.** The amino group is converted to ammonia, which can be excreted from the cell. Deamination results in the formation of an organic acid. Deamination of the amino acid phenylalanine can be detected by forming a colored ferric ion complex with the resulting acid (Figure 1). Deamination can also be ascertained by testing for the presence of ammonia using *Nessler's reagent*, which turns deep yellow in the presence of ammonia.

Various amino acids may be decarboxylated, yielding products that can be used for synthesis of other cellular components. **Decarboxylation** is the removal of

carbon dioxide from an amino acid. The presence of a specific decarboxylase enzyme results in the breakdown of the amino acid with the formation of the corresponding amine, liberation of carbon dioxide, and a shift in pH to alkaline. Media for decarboxylase reactions consist of glucose, nutrient broth, a pH indicator, and the desired amino acid. In Figure 2, bromcresol purple is used as a pH indicator, and a positive decarboxylase test yielding excess amines is indicated by purple. (Bromcresol purple is yellow in acidic conditions.) The names given to some of the amines, such as putrescine, indicate how foul smelling they are. Cadaverine was the name given to the foul-smelling diamine derived from decarboxylation of lysine in decomposing bodies on a battlefield.

Some bacteria liberate **hydrogen sulfide (H_2S)** from the sulfur-containing amino acids: cystine, cysteine, and methionine. H_2S can also be produced from the reduction of inorganic compounds, such as thiosulfate ($S_2O_3^{2-}$). H_2S is commonly called rotten-egg gas because of the copious amounts liberated when eggs decompose. To detect H_2S production, a heavy-metal salt containing ferrous ion (Fe^{2+}) is added to a nutrient culture medium. When H_2S is produced, the sulfide (S^{2-}) reacts with the metal salt to produce a visible black precipitate. The production of hydrogen sulfide from cysteine is shown in Figure 3.

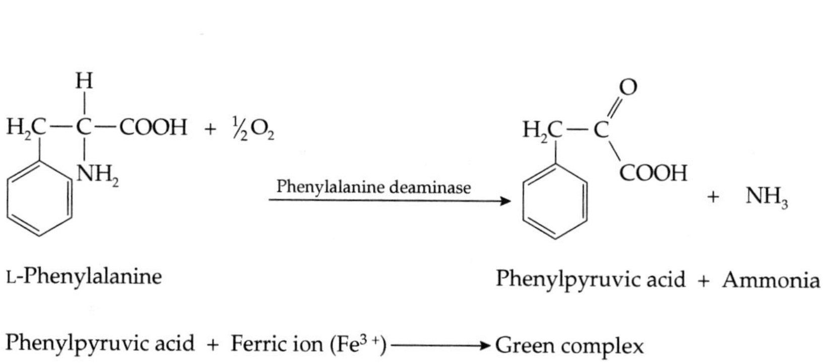

L-Phenylalanine

Phenylpyruvic acid + Ammonia

Phenylpyruvic acid + Ferric ion (Fe^{3+}) ⟶ Green complex

Figure 1

Phenylpyruvic acid resulting from the deamination of phenylalanine is detected by the addition of ferric ion (Fe^{3+}).

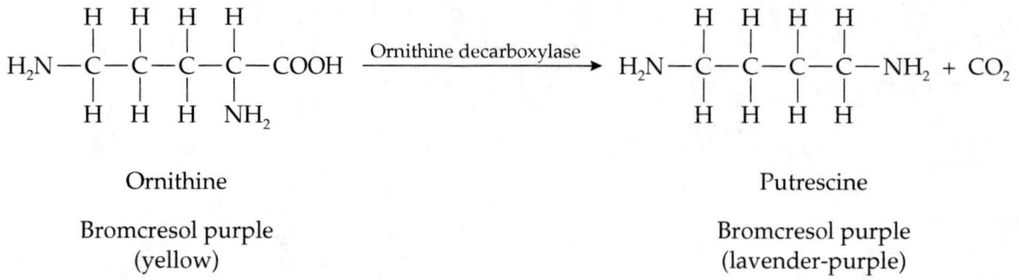

$$H_2N-\overset{\overset{\displaystyle H}{|}}{\underset{\underset{\displaystyle H}{|}}{C}}-\overset{\overset{\displaystyle H}{|}}{\underset{\underset{\displaystyle H}{|}}{C}}-\overset{\overset{\displaystyle H}{|}}{\underset{\underset{\displaystyle H}{|}}{C}}-\overset{\overset{\displaystyle H}{|}}{\underset{\underset{\displaystyle NH_2}{|}}{C}}-COOH \xrightarrow{\text{Ornithine decarboxylase}} H_2N-\overset{\overset{\displaystyle H}{|}}{\underset{\underset{\displaystyle H}{|}}{C}}-\overset{\overset{\displaystyle H}{|}}{\underset{\underset{\displaystyle H}{|}}{C}}-\overset{\overset{\displaystyle H}{|}}{\underset{\underset{\displaystyle H}{|}}{C}}-\overset{\overset{\displaystyle H}{|}}{\underset{\underset{\displaystyle H}{|}}{C}}-NH_2 + CO_2$$

Ornithine   Putrescine

Bromcresol purple   Bromcresol purple
(yellow)   (lavender-purple)

Figure 2

Decarboxylation of the amino acid ornithine causes a change in the bromcresol
purple indicator.

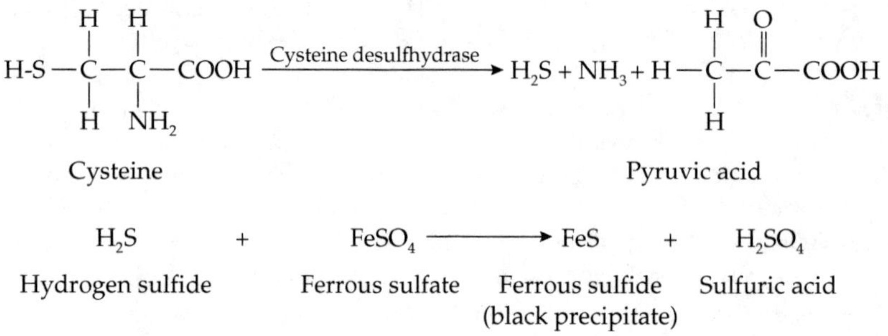

$$H-S-\overset{\overset{\displaystyle H}{|}}{\underset{\underset{\displaystyle H}{|}}{C}}-\overset{\overset{\displaystyle H}{|}}{\underset{\underset{\displaystyle NH_2}{|}}{C}}-COOH \xrightarrow{\text{Cysteine desulfhydrase}} H_2S + NH_3 + H-\overset{\overset{\displaystyle H}{|}}{\underset{\underset{\displaystyle H}{|}}{C}}-\overset{\overset{\displaystyle O}{\|}}{C}-COOH$$

Cysteine   Pyruvic acid

$$H_2S \quad + \quad FeSO_4 \longrightarrow FeS \quad + \quad H_2SO_4$$

Hydrogen sulfide   Ferrous sulfate   Ferrous sulfide   Sulfuric acid
                                       (black precipitate)

Figure 3

The release of H_2S from the amino acid cysteine is detected by the formation of
ferrous sulfide.

The ability of some bacteria to convert the amino acid tryptophan to indole or a blue compound called indigo is a useful diagnostic tool (Figure 4). The **indole test** is performed by inoculating a bacterium into tryptone broth and detecting indole by the addition of dimethylaminobenzaldehyde (**Kovacs reagent**). In this exercise, a differential screening medium, motility indole ornithine (MIO) agar, will be used. **MIO** is a single culture medium in which motility, indole production, and ornithine decarboxylase activity can be determined.

Materials

Phenylalanine slants (2)

Peptone iron deeps (2)

MIO deeps (2)

Second Period

Ferric chloride reagent

Kovacs reagent

Cultures (as needed)

Escherichia coli

Pseudomonas aeruginosa

Proteus vulgaris

Enterobacter aerogenes

Techniques Required

Inoculating loop technique

Aseptic technique

Procedure

Phenylalanine Deamination

1. Streak one phenylalanine slant heavily with *Proteus vulgaris* and the other with one of the remaining bacterial cultures.

2. Incubate the tubes for 1 to 2 days at 35°C. Observe for the presence of growth.

3. Add 4 or 5 drops of ferric chloride reagent to the top of the slant, allowing the reagent to run

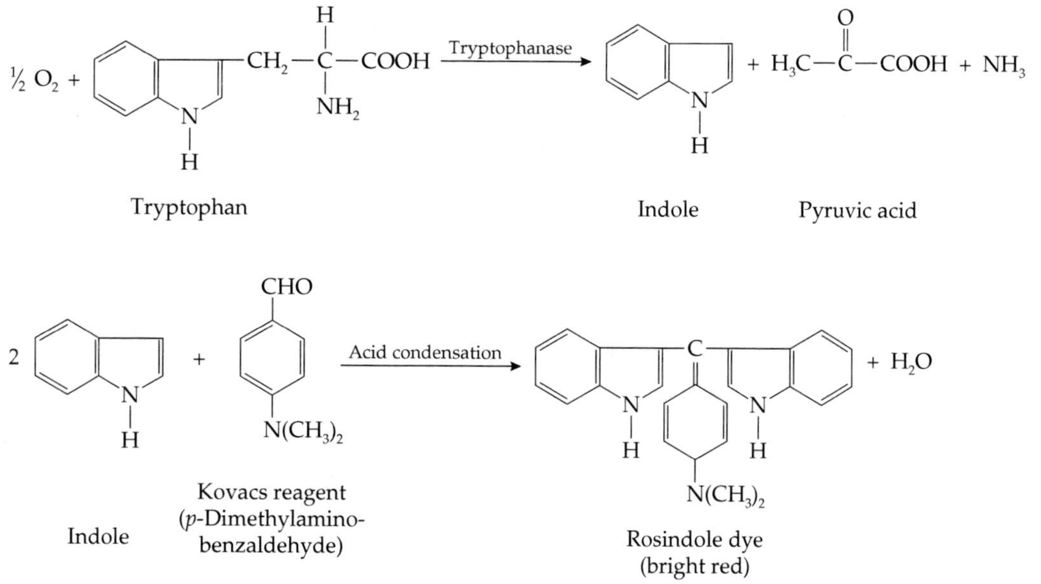

Figure 4

Many bacteria produce indole from the amino acid tryptophan.

through the growth on the slant. A positive test gives a dark green color.

Hydrogen Sulfide Production

1. Stab one peptone iron deep with *Escherichia coli* and the other with *Proteus vulgaris*.
2. Incubate the tubes at 35°C for up to 7 days. Observe initially at 24 or 48 hours.
3. Observe for the presence of growth. Blackening in the butt of the tube indicates a positive test.

MIO

1. Stab one MIO deep with *Enterobacter aerogenes* and the other with *Proteus vulgaris*.
2. Incubate the tubes for 24 hours at 35°C.

3. Compare the inoculated tube with an uninoculated tube. Observe for the presence of growth. Motility is demonstrated by growth diffusing out from the stab inoculation line or by clouding of the medium.
4. The ornithine decarboxylation reaction is indicated by a purple color; a negative is yellow. Why?

_____

_____

5. Add 4 to 5 drops of Kovacs reagent. Mix the tube gently. A cherry red color indicates a positive indole test.

Results

Record your results for each test in the Laboratory Report.

Protein Catabolism, Part 2

NAME _____

DATE _____

LAB SECTION _____

Purpose _____
_____
_____

Data

Fill in the following table.

	Test						MIO					
	Phenylalanine Deaminase			Hydrogen Sulfide			Motility		Indole		Ornithine Decarboxylase	
	Original color: _____			Original color: _____			Original color: _____					
Organism	Growth	Color	Reaction (+ or −)	Growth	Color	Reaction (+ or −)	Growth	Motility (+ or −)	Color	Reaction (+ or −)	Color	Reaction (+ or −)
Escherichia coli							Not tested		Not tested		Not tested	
Pseudomonas aeruginosa				Not tested			Not tested		Not tested		Not tested	
Proteus vulgaris												
Enterobacter aerogenes				Not tested								

Questions

1. When spoilage of canned foods occurs, what causes the blackening of the cans? _____
_____
_____
_____

2. Show how lysine could be decarboxylated to give the end-products indicated.

$$H_2N-\overset{\overset{\displaystyle H}{|}}{C}-\overset{\overset{\displaystyle H}{|}}{\underset{\underset{\displaystyle H}{|}}{C}}-\overset{\overset{\displaystyle H}{|}}{\underset{\underset{\displaystyle H}{|}}{C}}-\overset{\overset{\displaystyle H}{|}}{\underset{\underset{\displaystyle H}{|}}{C}}-\overset{\overset{\displaystyle H}{|}}{\underset{\underset{\displaystyle NH_2}{|}}{C}}-COOH \longrightarrow$$

Lysine   Cadaverine   +   _____

3. Show how alanine could be deaminated to give the end-products indicated.

$$H_2N-\overset{\overset{\displaystyle CH_3}{|}}{\underset{\underset{\displaystyle H}{|}}{C}}-COOH \longrightarrow$$

Alanine   Pyruvic acid   +   _____

Of what value is deamination to a microbe?

_____

Critical Thinking

1. Why look for black precipitate (FeS) in the butt instead of on the surface of an H_2S test?

2. Decarboxylation of an amino acid results in the evolution of carbon dioxide. Would a gas trap, such as that used in a fermentation test, be an accurate measure of decarboxylation?

3. In blue diaper syndrome, a baby's urine turns blue in its diapers following the administration of oral tryptophan. The baby's serum and urine levels of tryptophan are very low. What is causing the blue pigment indigo to appear?

Respiration

Objectives

After completing this exercise, you should be able to:

1. Define reduction.
2. Compare and contrast the following terms: aerobic respiration, anaerobic respiration, and fermentation.
3. Perform nitrate reduction, catalase, and oxidase tests.

Background

Molecules that combine with electrons liberated during metabolic processes are called **electron acceptors.** Electron acceptors become **reduced** when they gain electrons. Electrons are formed from the ionization of a hydrogen atom, as shown here:

$$H \longrightarrow H^+ + e^-$$

Hydrogen atom   Hydrogen ion   Electron

When an electron acceptor picks up an electron, it becomes negatively charged and combines with the positively charged hydrogen ion. **Reduction,** then, is a gain of electrons or hydrogen atoms.

Organic molecules act as electron acceptors in fermentative metabolism. Inorganic molecules serve as electron acceptors in oxidative metabolism or **respiration.** Molecular oxygen (O_2) is the final electron acceptor in **aerobic respiration.**

In aerobic bacteria, cytochromes carry electrons to O_2. Four general classes of bacterial cytochromes have been identified, and the **oxidase test** is used to determine the presence of one of these, cytochrome c. The oxidase test is useful in identifying bacteria.

During aerobic respiration, hydrogen atoms may combine with oxygen, forming hydrogen peroxide (H_2O_2), which is lethal to the cell. Most aerobic organisms produce the enzyme **catalase,** which breaks down hydrogen peroxide to water and oxygen, as shown here:

$$2H_2O_2 \xrightarrow{\text{Catalase}} 2H_2O + O_2\uparrow$$

Hydrogen peroxide   Water   Oxygen

In the process of **anaerobic respiration,** inorganic compounds other than O_2 act as final electron acceptors. (A few bacteria use organic electron acceptors in anaerobic respiration.) During anaerobic respiration, some bacteria reduce nitrates to nitrites; others further reduce nitrites to nitrous oxide, and some bacteria reduce nitrous oxide to nitrogen gas.

Nitrate broth (nutrient broth plus 0.1% potassium nitrate) is used to determine a bacterium's ability to reduce nitrates (Figure 1). Nitrites are detected by the addition of dimethyl-α-naphthylamine and sulfanilic acid to nitrate broth. A red color, indicating that nitrite is present, is a positive test for nitrate reduction. A negative test (no nitrites) is further checked for the presence of nitrate in the broth by the addition of zinc. If nitrates are present, reduction has not taken place. Zinc will reduce nitrate to nitrite, and a red color will appear. If neither nitrate nor nitrite is present, the nitrogen has been reduced to nitrous oxide (N_2O) or nitrogen gas (N_2).

The reduction of some inorganic compounds in respiration is shown in Figure 1. In this exercise, we will examine the reduction of nitrate, the catalase test, and the oxidase test.

Materials

Tubes containing nitrate broth (3)

Petri plates containing trypticase soy agar (2)

Second Period

Tube containing nitrate broth

Nitrate reagent A (dimethyl-α-naphthylamine)

Nitrate reagent B (sulfanilic acid)

Hydrogen peroxide, 3%

Sterile toothpick

Oxidase reagent, oxidase strip, or oxidase DrySlide

Zinc dust

Cultures

Bacillus subtilis

Escherichia coli

Pseudomonas aeruginosa

Lactococcus lactis

Techniques Required

Inoculating loop technique

Aseptic technique

From *Laboratory Experiments in Microbiology*, Eighth Edition, Ted R. Johnson and Christine L. Case. Copyright © 2006 by Pearson Education, Inc. Published by Benjamin Cummings, Inc. All rights reserved.

Aerobic respiration:

$$\tfrac{1}{2}O_2 + 2H^+ + 2e^- \longrightarrow H_2O$$

Oxygen   Water

Anaerobic respiration:

$$SO_4^{2-} + 10H^+ + 10e^- \longrightarrow H_2S + 4H_2O$$

Sulfate ion   Hydrogen sulfide

$$CO_3^{2-} + 10H^+ + 10e^- \longrightarrow CH_4 + 3H_2O$$

Carbonate ion   Methane

$$NO_3^- + 2H^+ + 2e^- \longrightarrow NO_2^- + H_2O \xrightarrow{6H^+ + 6e^-} N_2O \xrightarrow{2H^+ + 2e^-} N_2$$

Nitrate ion   Nitrite ion   Nitrous oxide   Nitrogen gas

Figure 1

Chemical equations showing the reduction of some electron acceptors in bacterial respiration.

Plate streaking

Carbohydrate catabolism

Procedure

Nitrate Reduction Test

1. Label three tubes of nitrate broth, and inoculate one with *Lactococcus*, one with *Pseudomonas*, and one with *Bacillus*.
2. Incubate the tubes at 35°C for 2 days. Examine the tubes for gas production.
3. Add 5 drops of nitrate A and 5 drops of nitrate B to each tube and to an uninoculated nitrate broth tube. Shake the tubes gently.
4. A red color within 30 seconds is a positive test. If the broth turns red, what compound is present?

_____

5. If it does not turn red, add a small pinch of zinc dust; if it turns red after 20–30 seconds, the test is negative. If not, it is positive for nitrate reduction. Why? _____

_____

6. Record your results.

Oxidase Test

1. Divide one plate in half. Label one half "*Escherichia*" and the other "*Pseudomonas*." Streak each organism on the appropriate half.
2. Incubate the plate, inverted, at 35°C for 24 to 48 hours.

3. To test for cytochrome oxidase, do one of the following:
   a. Drop oxidase reagent on the colonies and observe them for a color change to pink within 1 minute and then blue to black. Oxidase-negative colonies will not change color.
   b. Place an oxidase test strip in a Petri dish and moisten an area of the strip with water. Smear three or four well-isolated colonies onto the moistened area with a loop or a toothpick. Oxidase-positive bacteria will turn blue or purple within 10 to 20 seconds.
   c. Using a loop or toothpick, smear a little of one colony onto the oxidase DrySlide. Oxidase-positive bacteria will turn a dark-purple color within 2 minutes.

Catalase Test

1. Divide the other plate in half, and inoculate one half with *Lactococcus* and the other half with one short streak or spot of *Bacillus*.
2. Incubate the plate, inverted, at 35°C for 24 hours. After growth occurs, the plate may be kept at room temperature until the next lab period.
3. To test for catalase, do one of the following:
   a. Drop hydrogen peroxide on the colonies and observe them for bubbles.
   b. With a sterile toothpick, touch the center of a colony and transfer it to a clean glass slide. Discard the toothpick in the To Be Autoclaved area. Drop hydrogen peroxide on the organisms and observe them for bubbles (catalase-positive). What gas is in the bubbles?

_____

Respiration

NAME _____

DATE _____

LAB SECTION _____

Purpose _____

_____

_____

Data

Nitrate Reduction Test

Organism	Color After Adding Nitrate Reagents A and B	Color After Adding Zinc	Gas	NO_3^- Reduction
Uninoculated tube				
Lactococcus lactis				
Pseudomonas aeruginosa				
Bacillus subtilis				

Oxidase Test

Organism	Color After Adding Reagent	Oxidase Reaction
Escherichia coli		
Pseudomonas aeruginosa		

Catalase Test

Organism	Appearance After Adding H_2O_2	Catalase Reaction
Lactococcus lactis		
Bacillus subtilis		

Questions

1. Define reduction. _____

   _____

   _____

2. Why does hydrogen peroxide bubble when it is poured on a skin cut? _____

   _____

   _____

3. Differentiate between aerobic respiration and anaerobic respiration. _____

   _____

   _____

4. Differentiate between fermentation and anaerobic respiration. _____

   _____

   _____

Critical Thinking

1. Would nitrate reduction occur more often in the presence or absence of molecular oxygen? Explain.

2. In the nitrate reduction test, what does the presence of gas indicate?

3. Is nitrate reduction beneficial or harmful to farmers?

Rapid Identification Methods

Objectives

After completing this exercise, you should be able to:

1. Evaluate three methods of identifying enterics.
2. Name three advantages of the "systems approach" over conventional tube methods.

Background

The microbiology laboratory must identify bacteria quickly and accurately. Accuracy is improved by using a series of standardized tests. The IMViC tests were developed as a means of separating members of the Enterobacteriaceae (enterics)*, particularly the coliforms, to determine whether water was contaminated with sewage. The IMViC uses a standard combination of four tests, with each capital letter in **IMViC** representing a test; the i is added for easier pronunciation. The tests are as follows:

I for indole production from tryptophan

M for methyl red test for acid production from glucose

V for the Voges–Proskauer test for production of acetoin from glucose

C for the use of citrate as the sole carbon source

Although variation among strains does exist, IMViC reactions for selected species of the Enterobacteriaceae are given in Table 1.

Rapid identification methods have been developed that provide a large number of results from one inoculation. Examples are Enterotube II** and API 20E*** for identifying oxidase-negative, gram-negative bacteria belonging to the family Enterobacteriaceae. Enterotube II is divided into 12 compartments, each containing a different substrate in agar. A similar tube called Oxi/Ferm is used to identify oxidase-positive, gram-negative rods. API 20E consists of 20 microtubes

*Enterobacteriaceae are aerobic or facultatively anaerobic, gram-negative, nonendospore-forming, rod-shaped bacteria. Coliforms are Enterobacteriaceae that ferment lactose with acid and gas formation within 48 hours at 35°C.

**BD Bioscience, San Jose, CA 95131.

***bioMérieux, Inc., Durham, NC 27712.

Table 1

IMViC Reactions for Selected Species of the Enterobacteriaceae

Species	Indole	Methyl Red	Voges-Proskauer	Citrate
Escherichia coli	+(v)	+	−	−
Citrobacter freundii	−	+	−	+
Enterobacter aerogenes	−	−	+	+
Enterobacter cloacae	−	−	+	+
Serratia marcescens	−	+ or −*	+	+
Proteus vulgaris	+	+	−	−(v)
Proteus mirabilis	−	+	− or +**	+(v)

v = variable
*Majority of strains give + results
**Majority of strains give − results

containing dehydrated substrates. The substrates are rehydrated by adding a bacterial suspension. No culturing beyond the initial isolation is necessary with these systems. Comparisons between these rapid identification methods and conventional culture methods show that they are as accurate as conventional test-tube methods.

Computerized analysis of test results increases accuracy because each test is given a point value. Tests that are more important than others get more points. IMViC uses only four tests of equal value.

As commercial identification systems are developed, they can provide greater standardization in identification because they overcome the limitations of hunting through a key, preparing media, and evaluating tests within a laboratory or between different laboratories. They also save time, money, and labor.

Materials

Petri plate containing nutrient agar

Oxidase reagent

IMViC tests and reagents

Enterotube II and reagents

API 20E tray and reagents

Tube containing:

    5.0 ml sterile saline

    5-ml pipette

    Mineral oil

    Sterile Pasteur pipette

Culture

Unknown enteric #_____

Techniques Required

Inoculating loop and needle techniques

Aseptic technique

Plate streaking

MRVP tests

Fermentation tests

Protein catabolism

Respiration

Procedure

Isolation

1. Streak the nutrient agar plate with your unknown for isolation and to determine purity of the culture. Incubate the plate, inverted, at 35°C for 24 to 48 hours. Record the appearance of the colonies.
2. Determine the oxidase reaction of one of the colonies on the plate. Why?_____

    _____

    How will you determine the oxidase reaction? ___

    _____

    _____

IMViC Tests

1. Inoculate tubes of tryptone broth (indole test), MRVP broths, and Simmons citrate agar with your unknown.
2. Incubate the tubes at 35°C for 48 hours or longer; perform the appropriate tests. Add 4 to 5 drops of

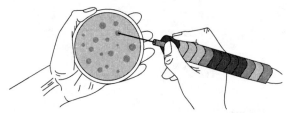

(a) Pick a well-isolated colony with the inoculating end of the wire.

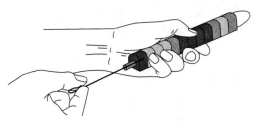

(b) Hold the bent end of the wire, and withdraw the needle through all 12 compartments with a turning motion.

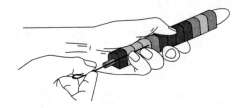

(c) Reinsert the wire through all 12 compartments. Then withdraw it to the notch on the wire. Break the wire at the notch.

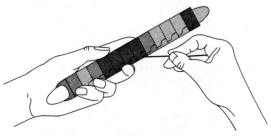

(d) Using the broken wire, punch holes through the foil covering the air inlets in the last eight compartments. Replace the caps loosely.

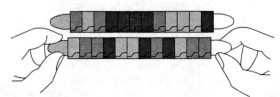

(e) After incubation, compare the tube to an uninoculated one to record results.

Figure 1

Inoculating an Enterotube II.

Table 2

Enterotube II Biochemical Reactions

Test	Comments	Indicator Changed	
		From	To
GLU	Acid from glucose	Red	Yellow
GAS	Gas produced from fermentation of glucose trapped in this compartment, causing separation of the wax		
LYS	Lysine decarboxylase	Yellow	Purple
ORN	Ornithine decarboxylase	Yellow	Purple
H_2S	Ferrous ion reacts with sulfide ions, forming a black precipitate		
IND	Kovacs reagent is added to the H_2S/IND compartment to detect indole	Beige	Red
ADON	Adonitol fermentation	Red	Yellow
LAC	Lactose fermentation	Red	Yellow
ARAB	Arabinose fermentation	Red	Yellow
SORB	Sorbitol fermentation	Red	Yellow
V–P	Voges–Proskauer reagents detect acetoin	Beige	Red
DUL	Dulcitol fermentation	Green	Yellow
PA	Phenylpyruvic acid released from phenylalanine after its deamination combines with iron salts to form a black precipitate		
UREA	Ammonia changes the pH of the medium	Yellow	Pink
CIT	Citric acid used as a carbon source	Green	Blue

Source: BD Bioscience, San Jose, CA 95131.

Kovacs reagent to the tryptone broth to test for indole. Mix the tube gently. A cherry red color indicates a positive test. Record your results.

Enterotube II (Figure 1)

1. Remove both caps from the Enterotube II. The straight end of the wire is used to pick up the inoculum; the bent end is the handle. Holding the Enterotube II, pick a well-isolated colony with the inoculating end of the wire (Figure 1a). Avoid touching the agar with the needle.

2. Inoculate the Enterotube II by holding the bent end of the wire and twisting; the tip of the wire should be visible in the citrate compartment. Withdraw the needle through all 12 compartments using a turning motion (Figure 1b).

3. Reinsert the needle into the Enterotube II, using a turning motion, through all 12 compartments until the notch on the wire is aligned with the opening of the tube. Break the wire at the notch by bending it (Figure 1c). The portion of the needle remaining

in the tube maintains anaerobic conditions necessary for fermentation, production of gas, and decarboxylation.

4. Punch holes with the broken-off wire through the foil covering the air inlets of the last eight compartments (adonitol through citrate) to provide aerobic conditions (Figure 1d). Replace the caps on both ends of the tube.

 Discard the wire in disinfectant.

5. Incubate the tube lying on its flat surface at 35°C for 24 hours.

6. Interpret and record all reactions (see Table 2) in the Laboratory Report. Read all the other tests *before* the indole test, which follows.

   a. Indole test. Place the Enterotube II horizontally and melt a small hole in the plastic film covering the H_2S/indole compartment by using a warm inoculating loop. Add 1 to 2 drops of

Rapid Identification Methods

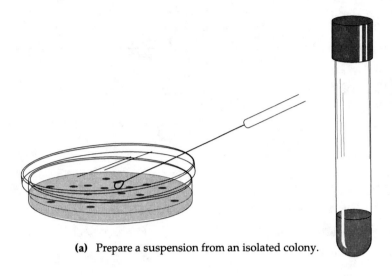

(a) Prepare a suspension from an isolated colony.

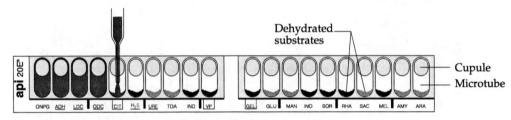

(b) Aseptically inoculate the microtubes with the bacterial suspension.
Carefully fill the tube and cupule sections of the CIT, VP, and GEL tubes (boxed tests).

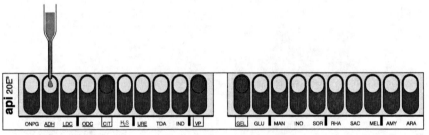

(c) Add mineral oil to the ADH, LDC, ODC, H$_2$S, and URE cupules (underlined tests).

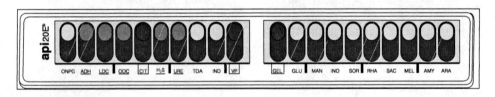

(d) Incubate the strip in its plastic tray.

Figure 2

Inoculating the API 20E system.

Kovacs reagent, and allow the reagent to contact the agar surface. A positive test is indicated by a red color within 10 seconds.

b. V–P test if needed. Add 2 drops of 20% KOH containing 5% α-naphthol to the V–P compartment. A positive test is indicated by development of a red color within 20 minutes.

7. Indicate each positive reaction by circling the number appearing below the appropriate compartment of the Enterotube II diagram in the Laboratory Report. Add the circled numbers only within each bracketed section, and enter this sum in the space provided below the arrow. The V–P test may be needed as a confirming test. Read the five numbers in these spaces across as a five-digit number in the *Computer Coding and Identification System.**

8. Dispose of the Enterotube II by placing it in the autoclave bag.

API 20E (Figure 2)

1. Prepare a bacterial suspension by touching the center of a well-isolated colony with a sterile loop and thoroughly mixing the inoculum in 5 ml of sterile saline (Figure 2a).

2. Place 5 ml of tap water into the corrugated incubation tray to provide a humid atmosphere during incubation.

3. Using a sterile Pasteur pipette, tilt the API 20E tray and fill the tube section of the microtubes with the bacterial suspension. Fill the tube *and* cupule sections of the CIT, VP, and GEL tubes (Figure 2b). Place the tip of the pipette against the side wall of the cupule and carefully inoculate without introducing bubbles into the cupule.

4. After inoculation, completely fill the cupule section of the ADH, LDC, ODC, H_2S, and URE tubes

with mineral oil to create anaerobic conditions (Figure 2c).

5. Place the plastic lid on the tray and incubate the strip for 24 hours at 35°C (Figure 2d). If the strip cannot be read after 24 hours, remove the strip from the incubator and refrigerate it.

6. Interpret and record all reactions (Table 3) in the Laboratory Report. Read all the other tests before the TDA, VP, and IND tests, which follow.

a. TDA test. Add 1 drop of 10% ferric chloride. A positive test is brownish-red. Indole-positive organisms may produce an orange color; this is a negative TDA reaction.

b. V–P test. Add 1 drop of V–P reagent II (KOH), and then 1 drop of V–P reagent I (α-napthol). A positive reaction produces a red color (not pale pink) after 10 minutes.

c. Indole test. Add 1 drop of Kovacs reagent. A red ring after 2 minutes indicates a positive reaction.

d. Nitrate reduction. Before adding reagents, look for bubbles in the GLU tube. Bubbles indicate reduction of nitrate to N_2. Add 2 drops of nitrate reagent A (dimethyl-α-napthylamine) and 2 drops of nitrate reagent B (sulfanilic acid). A positive reaction (red) may take 2 to 3 minutes to develop. A negative test can be confirmed by adding zinc dust.

7. Indicate each positive reaction with a (+) in the appropriate compartment of the Laboratory Report. Add the points for each positive reaction within each bold-outlined section. Read the seven numbers across as a seven-digit number in the *API 20E Analytical Profile Index.*** Nitrate reduction is a confirming test and not part of the seven-digit code.

8. Dispose of the API strip, tray, and lid by placing them in the autoclave bag.

---

*BD Bioscience, www.bd.com.

**bioMérieux, www.biomerieux-usa.com

Table 3

API 20E Biochemical Reactions

Test	Comments	Indicator	
		Positive	Negative
ONPG	O-nitrophenyl-β-D-galactopyranoside is hydrolyzed by the enzyme that hydrolyzes lactose	Yellow	Colorless
ADH	Arginine dihydrolase transforms arginine into ornithine, NH_3, and CO_2	Red	Yellow
LDC	Decarboxylation of lysine liberates cadaverine	Red	Yellow
ODC	Decarboxylation of ornithine produces putrescine	Red	Yellow
CIT	Citric acid used as sole carbon source	Dark blue	Light green
H_2S	Blackening indicates reduction of thiosulfate to H_2S	Black	No blackening
URE	Urea is hydrolyzed by the enzyme urease to NH_3 and CO_2	Red	Yellow
TDA	Deamination of tryptophan produces indole and pyruvic acid	Brown	Yellow
IND	Kovacs reagent is added to detect indole	Red ring	Yellow
VP	Addition of KOH and α-naphthol detects the presence of acetoin	Red	Colorless
GEL	Gelatin hydrolysis	Diffusion of pigment	No diffusion
GLU	Fermentation of glucose		
MAN	Fermentation of mannitol	Yellow or yellow-green	Blue or green
INO	Fermentation of inositol		
SOR	Fermentation of sorbitol		
RHA	Fermentation of rhamnose		
SAC	Fermentation of sucrose		
MEL	Fermentation of melibiose		
AMY	Fermentation of amygdalin		
ARA	Fermentation of arabinose		
NO_2, N_2 gas, N_2O	Nitrate reduction	Red Bubbles Yellow after addition of zinc	Yellow No bubbles Orange after reagents and zinc

Source: bioMérieux, Inc., Durham, NC 27712.

Rapid Identification Methods

NAME _____

DATE _____

LAB SECTION _____

Purpose _____

_____

_____

Data

Unknown # _____

Appearance on nutrient agar: _____

Oxidase reaction: _____

IMViC

Indicate positive (+) and negative (−) results for each test.

Indole: _____

Methyl red: _____

V–P: _____

Citrate: _____

Enterotube II

Circle the number corresponding to each positive reaction below the appropriate compartment. Then determine the five-digit code.

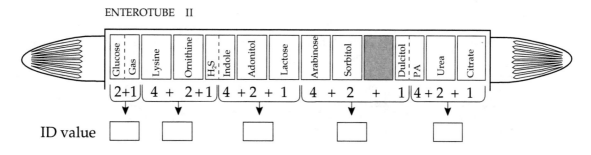

ENTEROTUBE II

V–P: _____

API 20E

Indicate positive (+) and negative (−) results in the Results line. Then determine the seven-digit code.

	ONPG 1	ADH 2	LDC 4	ODC 1	CIT 2	H₂S 4	URE 1	TDA 2	IND 4	VP 1	GEL 2	GLU 4
Results												
Profile number												

	MAN 1	INO 2	SOR 4	RHA 1	SAC 2	MEL 4	AMY 1	ARA 2	Oxi-dase 4	NO₂	N₂ gas
Results											
Profile number											

Questions

1. What species was identified in unknown # _____ by the IMViC tests? _____

   By the Enterotube II? _____

   By the API 20E? _____

2. Did all three methods agree? _____ If not, explain any discrepancies. _____

   _____

   _____

3. Which method did you prefer? _____ Why? _____

   _____

   _____

4. Why are systems developed to identify Enterobacteriaceae? _____

   _____

   _____

5. Why is an oxidase test performed on a culture before using API 20E and Enterotube II to identify the culture?

   _____

   _____

Critical Thinking

1. Why should the first digit in the five-digit Enterotube II ID value be equal to or greater than 2, and the fourth digit in the API 20E profile number be equal to or greater than 4?

2. Why can one species have two or more numbers in a rapid identification system? (For example, *E. coli* is Enterotube II numbers 34540 and 34560; *Citrobacter braakii* is API 20E numbers 3504552 and 3504553.)

3. Use Table 18.1 to give an example of a limitation of the IMViC tests.

Physical Methods of Control: Ultraviolet Radiation

Objectives

After completing this exercise, you should be able to:

1. Examine the effects of ultraviolet radiation on bacteria.
2. Explain the method of action of ultraviolet radiation and light repair of mutations.

Background

Radiant energy comes to the Earth from the Sun and other extraterrestrial sources, and some is generated on Earth from natural and human-made sources. The **radiant energy spectrum** is shown in Figure 1. Radiation differs in wavelength and energy. The shorter wavelengths have more energy. X rays and gamma rays are forms of **ionizing radiation.** Their principal effect is to ionize water into *highly reactive free radicals* (with unpaired electrons) that can break strands of DNA. The effect of radiation is influenced by many variables, such as the age of the cells, media composition, and temperature.

Some **nonionizing** wavelengths are essential for biochemical processes. The main absorption wavelengths for green algae, green plants, and photosynthetic bacteria are shown in Figure 1a. Animal cells synthesize vitamin D in the presence of light around 300 nm. Nonionizing radiation between 15 and 400 nm is called **ultraviolet (UV).** Wavelengths below 200 nm are absorbed by air and do not reach living organisms. The most lethal wavelengths, sometimes called biocidal, are in the **UVC** range, 200–290 nm. These wavelengths correspond to the optimal absorption wavelengths of DNA (Figure 1b). **UVB** wavelengths (290–320 nm) can also cause damage to DNA. **UVA** wavelengths (320–400 nm) are not as readily absorbed and are therefore less active on living organisms.

Ultraviolet light induces *thymine dimers* in DNA, which result in a mutation. Mutations in critical genes may result in the death of the cell unless the damage is repaired. When thymine dimers are exposed to visible light, *photolyases* are activated; these enzymes split the dimers, restoring the DNA to its undamaged state. This is called **light repair** or **photoreactivation.** Another repair mechanism, called **dark repair,** is independent of light. Dimers are removed by endonuclease, DNA polymerase replaces the nucleotides, and DNA ligase seals the sugar–phosphate backbone.

As a sterilizing agent, ultraviolet radiation is limited by its poor penetrating ability. It is used to sterilize some heat-labile solutions, to decontaminate hospital operating rooms and food-processing areas, and to disinfect wastewater.

In this exercise, we will investigate the penetrating ability of ultraviolet light and light repair by using lamps of the desired wavelength.

Materials

Petri plates containing nutrient agar (3)

Sterile cotton swabs (3)

Covers (choose one): Gauze; 3, 6, or 12 layers of paper; cloth; aluminum foil; clear glass; sunglasses; or plastic

Ultraviolet lamp (265 nm)

Plastic safety glasses

Cultures (as assigned)

Bacillus subtilis

Staphylococcus epidermidis

Micrococcus luteus

Techniques Required

Aseptic technique

Procedure

1. Swab the surface of each plate with *one* of the cultures; to ensure complete coverage, swab the surface in two directions. Label the plates "A," "B," and "C."
2. Remove the lid of an inoculated plate and cover one-half of the plate with one of the covering materials (Figure 2). Cover one-half of each of the remaining plates with the same material.

> **Do not look at the ultraviolet light, and do not leave your hand exposed to it. Wear safety glasses.**

From *Laboratory Experiments in Microbiology*, Eighth Edition, Ted R. Johnson and Christine L. Case. Copyright © 2006 by Pearson Education, Inc. Published by Benjamin Cummings, Inc. All rights reserved.

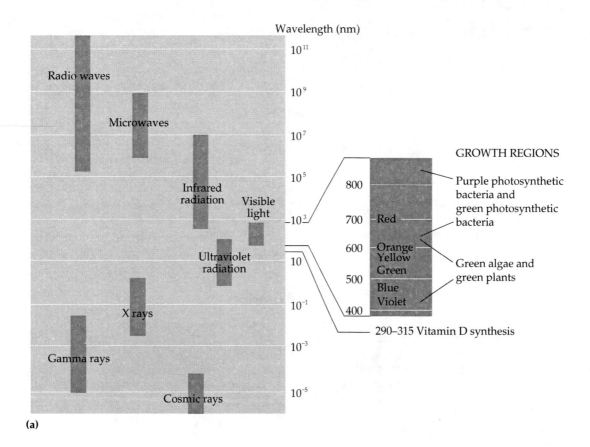

(a)

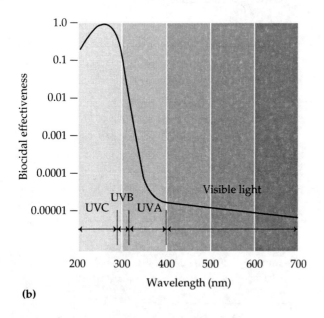

(b)

Figure 1

Radiant energy. **(a)** Radiant energy spectrum and absorption of light for growth.
(b) Biocidal effectiveness of radiant energy between 200 and 700 nanometers (nm)
(from UV to visible red light).

3. Place each plate directly under the ultraviolet light 24 cm from the light with the *lid off,* agar-side up, with the covering material on one-half of the plate. Why should the lid be removed? _____

_____

Plate A: Expose to UV light for 30 seconds. Remove the covering material, replace the lid, and incubate in a dark environment at room temperature.

Plate B: Expose to UV light for 30 seconds. Remove the covering material and replace the Petri plate lid. Incubate in sunlight or under lights at room temperature.

Plate C: Expose for 60 seconds. Remove covering material, replace the lid, and incubate in a dark environment at room temperature.

4. Incubate all three plates at room temperature until the next period.

5. Examine all plates and record your results. Observe the results of students using the other organisms.

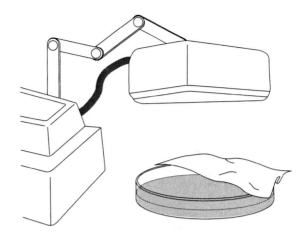

Figure 2

With the lid removed, cover one-half of an inoculated Petri plate with one of the covering materials.

LABORATORY REPORT

Physical Methods of Control: Ultraviolet Radiation

NAME _____

DATE _____

LAB SECTION _____

Purpose _____

_____

_____

Data

What organism did you use? _____

What did you use to cover one-half of each plate? _____

Sketch your results. Note any pigmentation.

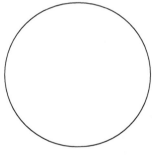
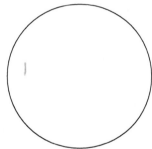
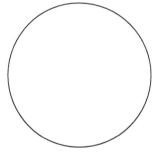

| A | B | C |

Classmates' results:

Bacterium						
Plate	A	B	C	A	B	C
Amount of growth on UV-exposed area						
Pigment						

Conclusions _____

_____

_____

Questions

1. If the *Bacillus* had sporulated before exposure to radiation, would that affect the results? _____

   _____

   _____

2. What are the variables in ultraviolet radiation treatment? _____

   _____

   _____

3. Many of the microorganisms found on environmental surfaces are pigmented. Of what possible advantage is

   the pigment?_____

   _____

   _____

Critical Thinking

1. Can dark repair be a factor in this experiment?

2. Why are there still some colonies growing in the areas exposed to ultraviolet light?

3. How might the results differ if a UVA lamp were used? A UVB lamp?

4. Considering your results, discuss the possible effects of UV radiation on the ecology of a lake if the UV radiation has the same effect on the lake bacteria as it did on the bacteria in your experiment.

Physical Methods of Control: Heat

The successful man lengthens his stride when he discovers that the signpost has deceived him; the failure looks for a place to sit down.

JOHN R. ROGERS

Objectives

After completing this exercise, you should be able to:

1. Compare the bactericidal effectiveness of dry heat and moist heat.
2. Evaluate the heat tolerance of microbes.
3. Define and provide a use for each of the following: incineration, hot-air oven, pasteurization, boiling, and autoclaving.

Background

The use of extreme temperature to control the growth of microbes is widely employed. Generally, if heat is applied, microbes are killed; if cold temperatures are used, microbial growth is inhibited.

Bacteria exhibit different tolerances to the application of heat. Heat sensitivity is genetically determined and is partially reflected in the *optimal* growth ranges, which are **psychrophilic** (about 15°C), **psychrotrophic** (20°C to 30°C), **mesophilic** (25°C to 40°C), **ther-**

mophilic (45°C to 65°C), **hyperthermophilic** (about 80°C or higher), and by the presence of heat-resistant endospores (Figure 1). Overall, bacteria are more heat resistant than most other forms of life. Heat sensitivity of organisms can be affected by container size, cell density, moisture content, pH, and medium composition.

Heat can be applied as dry or moist heat. **Dry heat,** such as that in hot-air ovens or incineration (for example, flaming loops), denatures enzymes, dehydrates microbes, and kills by oxidation effects. A standard application of dry heat in a hot-air oven is 170°C for 2 hours. The heat of hot air is not readily transferred to a cooler body such as a microbial cell. Moisture transfers heat energy to the microbial cell more efficiently than dry air, resulting in the denaturation of enzymes. **Moist heat** methods include pasteurization, boiling, and autoclaving. In **pasteurization** the temperature is maintained at 63°C for 30 minutes or 72°C for 15 seconds to kill designated organisms that are pathogenic or cause spoilage. **Boiling** (100°C) for 10 minutes will kill

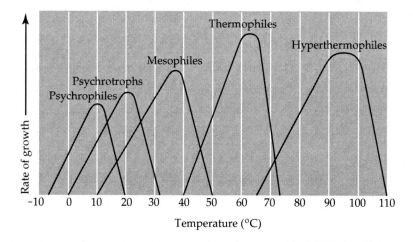

Figure 1

Typical growth responses of different types of microorganisms to temperature.

Table 1

Relationship Between Pressure and Temperature of Steam

Pressure (pounds per square inch, psi, in excess of atmospheric pressure)	Temperature (°C)
0 psi	100°C
5 psi	110°C
10 psi	116°C
15 psi	121°C
20 psi	126°C
30 psi	135°C

Source: G. J. Tortora, B. R. Funke, and C. L. Case. *Microbiology: An Introduction,* 9th ed. San Francisco, CA: Benjamin Cummings, 2007.

vegetative bacterial cells; however, endospores are not inactivated. The most effective method of moist heat sterilization is **autoclaving,** the use of steam under pressure. Increased pressure raises the boiling point of water and produces steam with a higher temperature (Table 1). Standard conditions for autoclaving are 15 psi, at 121°C, for 15 minutes. This is usually sufficient to kill endospores and render materials sterile.

There are two different methods of measuring heat effectiveness. **Thermal death time (TDT)** is the length of time required to kill all bacteria in a liquid culture at a given temperature. The less common **thermal death point (TDP)** is the temperature required to kill all bacteria in a liquid culture in 10 minutes.

Materials

Petri plates containing nutrient agar (2)

Thermometer

Empty tube

Beaker

Hot plate or tripod and asbestos pad

Ice

Cultures (as assigned)

Group A:

> Old (48 to 72 hours) *Bacillus subtilis*
> Young (24 hours) *Bacillus subtilis*

Group B:

> *Staphylococcus epidermidis*

> *Escherichia coli*

Group C:

> Young (24 hours) *Bacillus subtilis*
> *Escherichia coli*

Group D:

> Mold (*Penicillium*) spore suspension
> Old (48 to 72 hours) *Bacillus subtilis*

Demonstration

Autoclaved and dry-heated soil

Techniques Required

Inoculating loop technique

Aseptic technique

Plate streaking

Graphing

Procedure

Each pair of students is assigned two cultures and a temperature.

Group		Group	
A: 63°C	_____	A: 72°C	_____
B: 63°C	_____	B: 72°C	_____
C: 63°C	_____	C: 72°C	_____
D: 63°C	_____	D: 72°C	_____

You can share beakers of water as long as the effect of the same temperature is being evaluated.

1. Divide two plates of nutrient agar into five sections each. Label the sections "0," "30 sec," "2 min," "5 min," and "15 min."

2. Set up a water bath in the beaker, with the water level higher than the level of the broth in the tubes. Do not put the broth tubes into the water bath at this time. Carefully put the thermometer in a test tube of water in the bath.

3. Streak the assigned organisms on the "0" time section of the appropriate plate. Why are we using "old" and "young" *Bacillus* cultures? _____

    _____

4. Raise the temperature of the bath to the desired temperature and maintain that temperature. Use ice to adjust the temperature. Why was 63°C selected as one of the temperatures? _____

5. Place the broth tubes of your organism into the bath when the temperature is at the desired point. After 30 seconds, remove the tubes, resuspend the culture, streak a loopful on the corresponding sections, and return the tubes to the water bath. Repeat at 2, 5, and 15 minutes. What is the longest time period that any microbe is exposed to heat?

_____

6. When you are done, clean the beaker and return the materials. Incubate the plates, inverted, at 35°C until the next lab period. Record your results and the results for the other organisms tested: $(-) =$ no growth, $(+) =$ minimum growth, $(2+) =$ moderate growth, $(3+) =$ heavy growth, and $(4+) =$ maximum growth.

7. Examine the demonstration plates and record your observations. Collect results from your classmates to complete the data table in your Laboratory Report.

Physical Methods of Control: Heat

NAME _____

DATE _____

LAB SECTION _____

Purpose _____

_____

_____

Data

Record growth on a scale from (−) to (4+).

Organism	Temperature/Time									
	63°C					72°C				
	0	30 sec	2 min	5 min	15 min	0	30 sec	2 min	5 min	15 min
Old *Bacillus subtilis*										
Young *Bacillus subtilis*										
Staphylococcus epidermidis										
Escherichia coli										
Mold (*Penicillium*) spores										

Demonstration Plates

	Control	Autoclaved	Dry-Heated
Number of colonies			
Number of different colonies			

Use a computer graphing application to graph the effect of heating on each organism or draw your graphs below.

Graph your cultures at ___°C.

Organism _____   Organism _____

(Graph: Growth (y-axis 0–4) vs Time (min), x-axis)

(Graph: Growth (y-axis 0–4) vs Time (min), x-axis)

Conclusions _____

_____

_____

_____

Questions

1. Compare the heat sensitivity of fungal spores to that of bacterial endospores. _____

_____

2. Compare the effectiveness of autoclaving and dry heat. _____

_____

_____

_____

3. Give an example of an application (use) of thermal death time. _____

_____

4. In the exercise, was the thermal death time or thermal death point determined?_____

_____

5. Give an example of a nonlaboratory use of each of the following methods to control microbial growth:

   a. Incineration: _____

   b. Pasteurization: _____

   c. Autoclaving: _____

6. Define pasteurization. What is the purpose of pasteurization? _____

_____

_____

_____

Critical Thinking

1. Explain why fungi and *Bacillus* sometimes grow better after heat treatment.

2. The decimal reduction time (DRT) is the time it takes to kill 90% of cells present. Assume that a DRT value for autoclaving a culture is 1.5 minutes. How long would it take to kill all the cells if 10^6 cells were present? What would happen if you stopped the heating process at 9 minutes?

3. Indicators are used in autoclaving to ensure that sterilization is complete. One type of chemical indicator turns color when it has reached a specific temperature; the other type turns color when it has reached a specified temperature and been exposed to steam. Which type of indicator should be used?

4. A biological indicator used in autoclaving is a vial containing 10^9 *Geobacillus stearothermophilus* cells that is placed in the autoclave with the material to be sterilized. After autoclaving, the vial is incubated and examined for growth. Why is this species used as opposed to *E. coli* or *G. subtilis*?

Chemical Methods of Control: Disinfectants and Antiseptics

*One nineteenth-century method of avoiding
cholera: Wear a pouch of foul-smelling herbs
around your neck. If the odor is bad enough,
disease carriers will spare you the trouble of avoiding them.*

ANONYMOUS

Objectives

After completing this exercise, you should be able to:

1. Define the following terms: disinfectant and anti-septic.
2. Describe the use-dilution test.
3. Evaluate the relative effectiveness of various chemical substances as antimicrobial agents.

Background

A wide variety of chemicals called **antimicrobial agents** are available for controlling the growth of microbes. Chemotherapeutic agents are used internally and will be evaluated in another exercise. **Disinfectants** are chemical agents used on inanimate objects to lower the level of microbes on their surfaces; **antiseptics** are chemicals used on living tissue to decrease the number of microbes. Disinfectants and antiseptics affect bacteria in many ways. Those that result in bacterial death are called **bactericidal agents.** Those causing temporary inhibition of growth are **bacteriostatic agents.**

No single chemical is the best to use in all situations. Antimicrobial agents must be matched to specific organisms and environmental conditions. Additional variables to consider in selecting an antimicrobial agent include pH, solubility, toxicity, organic material present, and cost. In evaluating the effectiveness of antimicrobial agents, the concentration, length of contact, and whether it is lethal (*-cidal*) or inhibiting (*-static*) are the important criteria. The standard method for measuring the effectiveness of a chemical agent is the **American Official Analytical Chemist's use-dilution test.** For most purposes, three strains of bacteria are used in this test: *Salmonella enterica* Choleraesuis, *Staphylococcus aureus*, and *Pseudomonas aeruginosa*. To perform a use-dilution test, metal rings are dipped into standardized cultures of the test bacteria grown in liquid media, removed, and dried. The rings are then placed into a solution of the disinfectant at the concentration recommended by the manufacturer for 10 minutes at 20°C. The rings are then transferred to a nutrient medium to permit the growth of any surviving bacteria. The effectiveness of the disinfectant can then be determined by the amount of resulting growth. The use-dilution test is limited to bactericidal compounds and cannot be used to evaluate bacteriostatic compounds.

In this exercise, we will perform a modified use-dilution test.

Materials

Petri plates containing nutrient agar (2)

Sterile water

Sterile tubes (3)

Sterile 5-ml pipettes (2)

Sterile 1-ml pipettes (2)

Test substance: chemical agents such as bathroom cleaner, floor cleaner, mouthwash, lens cleaner, and acne cream. Bring your own.

Culture

Staphylococcus aureus

Techniques Required

Inoculating loop technique

Aseptic technique

Pipetting

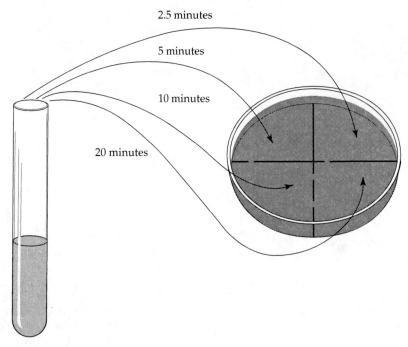

2.5 minutes

5 minutes

10 minutes

20 minutes

Chemical and bacteria

Figure 1

Transfer a loopful from the tube containing the chemical and *Staphylococcus* to the
appropriate sector at the time intervals shown. Repeat the procedure with a loopful
from the tube containing the test substance and *Staphylococcus* onto the appropriate
sector of the second nutrient agar plate.

Procedure

1. Using sterile water, prepare a dilution of the test
   substance in a sterile tube, diluted to the strength
   at which it is normally used. If it is a paste, it must
   be suspended in sterile water.

2. Transfer 5 ml of the diluted test substance to a sterile tube. If the test substance is normally used at
   full strength, then don't dilute it for this experiment. Label the tube. Add 5 ml of your laboratory
   disinfectant to another sterile tube. What is the disinfectant you use to disinfect your lab bench?

   _____

   Label the tube.

3. Divide one plate of nutrient agar into five sections.
   Label the sections "0," "D-2.5," "D-5," "D-10," and
   "D-20." The D stands for laboratory disinfectant.

4. Label the other nutrient agar plate for the other
   chemical and divide it into four sections. Label the
   sections "2.5," "5," "10," and "20."

5. Inoculate the 0 sector with a loopful of S. *aureus*.

6. Aseptically add 0.5 ml of the S. *aureus* culture to
   each tube prepared in step 2.

7. Transfer one loopful from each tube to a corresponding sector at 2.5 minutes, 5 minutes, 10 minutes, and 20 minutes (Figure 1).

8. Incubate the plates, inverted, at 35°C until the
   next lab period. (Discard the chemical/bacteria
   mixtures in the To Be Autoclaved area.)

9. Observe the plates for growth. Record the growth
   as (−) = no growth, (+) = minimum growth,
   (2+) = moderate growth, (3+) = heavy growth,
   and (4+) = maximum growth.

Chemical Methods of Control: Disinfectants and Antiseptics

NAME _____

DATE _____

LAB SECTION _____

Purpose _____

_____

_____

Data

Time of Exposure (min)	Amount of Growth		
	Control	Lab Disinfectant	Chemical: _____
0			
2.5			
5			
10			
20			

Conclusions _____

_____

_____

Questions

1. Was this a fair test? Is it representative of the effectiveness of the test substance? _____

_____

_____

2. Read the label of the preparation you tested. What is (are) the active ingredient(s)? _____

_____

Using your textbook or another reference, find the method of action of the active ingredient(s) in the test substance.

_____

_____

_____

3. What is the use-dilution method? _____

_____

_____

Critical Thinking

1. How could the procedures used in this experiment be altered to measure bacteriostatic effects?

2. In the use-dilution test, a chemical is evaluated by its ability to kill 10^6 to 10^8 dried *Clostridium sporogenes* or *Bacillus subtilis* endospores. Why is this considered a stringent test?

3. The effectiveness of disinfectants can be measured in DRT values. DRT, or decimal reduction time, is the length of time it takes to kill 90% of a test population of bacteria. The DRT values for contact lens disinfectants against *Serratia marcescens* are as follows:

Disinfectant	DRT Value (min)	Disinfectant	DRT Value (min)
Chlorhexidine, 0.005%	2.8	Thimerosal, 0.002%	138.9
Hydrogen peroxide, 3%	3.1	Polyquaternium-1, 0.001%	383.3

Which disinfectant is most effective? _____ What is the minimum time that lenses with 10^2

bacteria should be soaked in chlorhexidine? _____

In polyquaternium-1? _____ What if the lenses are contaminated with *Staphylococcus* or

Acanthamoeba? _____

_____

Why isn't a higher concentration of disinfectant used? _____

Chemical Methods of Control: Antimicrobial Drugs

The aim of medicine is to prevent disease and prolong life; the ideal of medicine is to eliminate the need of a physician.

WILLIAM JAMES MAYO

Objectives

After completing this exercise, you should be able to:

1. Define the following terms: antibiotic, antimicrobial agent, and MIC.
2. Perform an antibiotic sensitivity test.
3. Provide the rationale for the agar diffusion technique.

Background

The observation that some microbes inhibited the growth of others was made as early as 1874. Pasteur and others observed that infecting an animal with *Pseudomonas aeruginosa* protected the animal against *Bacillus anthracis*. Later investigators coined the word **antibiosis** (against life) for this inhibition and called the inhibiting substance an **antibiotic.** In 1928, Alexander Fleming observed antibiosis around a *Penicillium* mold growth on a culture of staphylococci. He found that culture filtrates of *Penicillium* inhibited the growth of many gram-positive cocci and *Neisseria* spp. In 1940, Selman A. Waksman isolated the antibiotic streptomycin, produced by an actinomycete. This antibiotic was effective against many bacteria that were not affected by penicillin. Actinomycetes remain an important source of antibiotics. Today, research investigators look for antibiotic-producing actinomycetes and fungi in soil and have synthesized many antimicrobial substances in the laboratory. Antimicrobial chemicals absorbed or used internally, whether natural (antibiotics) or synthetic, are called **antimicrobial agents.**

A physician or dentist needs to select the correct antimicrobial agent intelligently and administer the appropriate dose in order to treat an infectious disease; then the practitioner must follow that treatment in order to be aware of resistant forms of the organism that might occur. The clinical laboratory isolates the **pathogen** (disease-causing organism) from a clinical sample and determines its sensitivity to antimicrobial agents.

In the **disk-diffusion method,** a Petri plate containing an agar growth medium is inoculated uniformly over its entire surface. Paper disks impregnated with various antimicrobial agents are placed on the surface of the agar. During incubation, the antimicrobial agent *diffuses* from the disk, from an area of high concentration to an area of lower concentration. An effective agent will inhibit bacterial growth, and measurements can be made of the size of the **zones of inhibition** around the disks. The concentration of antimicrobial agent at the edge of the zone of inhibition represents its **minimum inhibitory concentration (MIC).** The MIC is determined by comparing the zone of inhibition with MIC values in a standard table (Table 1). The MIC values are determined by doing a broth dilution test in a laboratory by using a test bacterium. The zone size is affected by such factors as the diffusion rate of the antimicrobial agent and the growth rate of the organism. To minimize the variance between laboratories, the standardized **Kirby-Bauer test** for agar diffusion methods is performed in many clinical laboratories with strict quality controls. This test uses *Mueller-Hinton agar.* Mueller-Hinton agar allows the antimicrobial agent to diffuse freely.

In this exercise, we will evaluate antimicrobial agents by the disk-diffusion method.

Materials

Petri plate containing Mueller-Hinton agar

Sterile cotton swab

Dispenser and antimicrobial disks

Forceps

Alcohol

Ruler (second period)

Cultures (as assigned)

Staphylococcus aureus broth

Escherichia coli broth

Pseudomonas aeruginosa broth

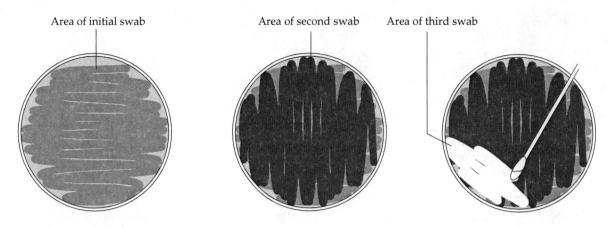

Figure 1

Dip a cotton swab in the culture to be tested and swab across the surface of the agar without leaving any gaps. Using the same swab, swab the agar in a direction perpendicular to the first inoculum. Repeat, swabbing the agar at a 45° angle to the first inoculum.

Techniques Required

Inoculating loop technique, Exercise 10

Aseptic technique, Exercise 10

Procedure

1. Aseptically swab the assigned culture onto the appropriate plate. Swab in three directions to ensure complete plate coverage (Figure 1). Why is complete coverage essential? _____

    _____

    Let stand at least 5 minutes.
2. Follow procedure a or b.
    a. Place the antimicrobial-impregnated disks by pushing the dispenser over the agar. Sterilize your loop and touch each disk with the sterile inoculating loop to ensure better contact with the agar. Record the agents and the disk codes in your Laboratory Report. Circle the corresponding chemicals in Table 1.
    b. Sterilize forceps by dipping them in alcohol and burning off the alcohol.

 While it is burning, hold the forceps pointed down. Keep the beaker of alcohol away from the flame.

Obtain a disk impregnated with a antimicrobial agent and place it on the surface of the agar (Figure 2a). Gently tap the disk with

(a) Place disks impregnated with antimicrobial agents on an inoculated culture medium with sterile forceps to get the pattern shown in **(b)**.

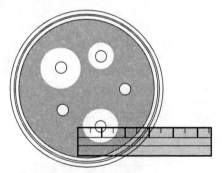

(b) After incubation, measure the diameters of zones of inhibition.

Figure 2

Disk-diffusion method.

the forceps to ensure better contact with the agar. Repeat, placing five to six different disks the same distance apart on the Petri plate. See the location of the disks in Figure 2b. Record the agents and the disk codes in your

Table 1

Interpretation of Inhibition Zones of Test Cultures

Disk Symbol	Antimicrobial Agent	Disk Content	Diameter of Zones of Inhibition (mm)		
			Resistant	Intermediate	Susceptible
AM	Ampicillin when testing gram-negative bacteria	10 µg	<13	14–16	>17
	Ampicillin when testing gram-positive bacteria	10 µg	<28	—	>29
C	Chloramphenicol	30 µg	<12	13–17	>18
CAZ	Ceftazidime	30 µg	<14	15–17	>18
CB	Carbenicillin	100 µg	<19	—	>23
	Carbenicillin when testing *Pseudomonas*	100 µg	<13	—	>17
CF	Cephalothin	30 µg	<14	—	>18
CIP	Ciprofloxacin	5 µg	<15	16–20	>21
E	Erythromycin	15 µg	<13	14–22	>23
Fox	Cefoxitin (Mefoxin)	30 µg	<14	—	>18
G	Sulfisoxazole (Gantrisin)	300 µg	<12	13–16	>17
GM	Gentamicin	10 µg	<12	13–14	>15
IPM	Imipenem	10 µg	<13	14–15	>16
P	Penicillin G when testing staphylococci	10 units	<28	—	>29
	Penicillin G when testing other bacteria	10 units	<14	—	>15
R	Rifampin	5 µg	<16	17–19	>20
S	Streptomycin	10 µg	<11	12–14	>15
SxT	Trimethoprim/ Sulfamethoxazole	1.25 µg/ 23.75 µg	<10	11–15	>16
Te	Tetracycline	30 µg	<14	15–18	>19
VA	Vancomycin	30 µg	<9	10–11	>12
	Vancomycin when testing enterococci	30 µg	<14	15–16	>17

Source: National Committee for Clinical Laboratory Standards. Performance Standards for Antimicrobial Disk Susceptibility Tests.

Laboratory Report. Circle the corresponding chemicals in Table 1.

3. Incubate the plate, inverted, at 35°C until the next period. Measure the zones of inhibition in millimeters, using a ruler on the underside of the plate (Figure 2b). If the diameter is difficult to measure, the radius from the center of the disk to the edge of the zone can be measured. Multiply the radius by 2 to get the diameter of the zone. Record the zone size and, based on the values in Table 1, indicate whether the organism is susceptible, intermediate, or resistant. Record the results of students using the other two bacteria.

Effectiveness of Hand Scrubbing

People are sick because they are poor; they become poorer because they are sick, and they become sicker because they are poorer.

ANONYMOUS

Objectives

After completing this exercise, you should be able to:

1. Evaluate the effectiveness of handwashing and a surgical scrub.
2. Explain the importance of aseptic technique in the hospital environment.

Background

The skin is sterile during fetal development. After birth, a baby's skin is colonized by many bacteria for the rest of its life. As an individual ages and changes environments, the microbial population changes to match the environmental conditions. The microorganisms that are more or less permanent are called **normal microbiota.** Microbes that are present only for days or weeks are referred to as **transient microbiota.**

Discovery of the importance of handwashing in disease prevention is credited to Ignaz Semmelweis at Vienna General Hospital in 1846. He noted that the lack of aseptic methods was directly related to the incidence of puerperal fever and other diseases. Medical students would go directly from the autopsy room to the patient's bedside and assist in child delivery without washing their hands. Less puerperal sepsis occurred in patients attended by midwives, who did not touch cadavers. Semmelweis established a policy for the medical students of handwashing with a chloride of lime solution that resulted in a drop in the death rate due to puerperal sepsis from 12% to 1.2% in one year. Guidelines from the Centers for Disease Control and Prevention state that "handwashing is the single most important procedure for preventing nosocomial infections," yet recent studies in hospitals show handwashing rates as low as 31%.

A layer of oil and the structure of the skin prevent the removal of all bacteria by handwashing. Soap helps remove the oil, and scrubbing will maximize the removal of bacteria. Hospital procedures require personnel to wash their hands before attending a patient, and a complete surgical scrub—removing the transient and many of the resident microbiota—is done before surgery. Transient microbiota are usually removed after 10 to 15 minutes of scrubbing with soap. The surgeon's skin is never sterilized. Only burning or scraping it off would achieve that.

In this exercise, we will examine the effectiveness of washing skin with soap and water. Only organisms capable of growing aerobically on nutrient agar will be observed. Because organisms with different nutritional and environmental requirements will not grow, this procedure will involve only a minimum number of the skin microbiota.

Materials

Petri plates containing nutrient agar (2)

Scrub brush

Bar soap or liquid soap (bring one from home)

Waterless hand cleaner

Techniques Required

Colony morphology

Procedure

1. Select two nutrient agar plates.
   a. Divide one nutrient agar plate into four quadrants. Label the sections 1 through 4. Label the plate "Water." _____
   b. Divide the other nutrient agar plate into five sections. Label the sections 1 through 5. Label the plate "Soap." Which soap will you use? _____
2. Use the "Water" plate first. Touch section 1 with your fingers, wash well *without* soap, shake off excess water, and, while your hands are still wet, touch section 2. Do not dry your fingers with a towel. Wash

again, and, while your hands are still wet, touch section 3. Wash a final time, and touch section 4. Touch the same fingers to the plate each time.

3. Use your same hand on the plate labeled "Soap." Wash well with soap, rinse, shake off the excess water, and then touch section 1.

4. Wash again with soap, rinse, shake off the excess water, and then touch section 2.

5. Using a brush and soap, scrub your hand for 2 minutes, rinse, and shake off the excess water; then touch section 3.

6. Repeat the soap-and-brush scrub for 4 minutes, rinse, and shake off the excess water; then touch section 4.

7. Use a waterless hand-cleaning product; then touch section 5. What are the active ingredients in the product? _____

8. Incubate the plates, inverted, at 35°C until the next period.

9. Speculate on your expected results, and record them in your Laboratory Report.

10. Record the growth as (−) = no growth, (+) = minimum growth, (2+) = moderate growth, (3+) = heavy growth, and (4+) = maximum growth.

Effectiveness of Hand Scrubbing

NAME _____

DATE _____

LAB SECTION _____

Purpose _____

_____

_____

Expected Results

Before the next lab period, indicate the relative amounts of growth you *expect* in each quadrant.

Section	Water Alone	Soap
1.	(No washing)	
2.		
3.		
4.		
5.		(Waterless hand cleaner)

Data

Indicate the relative amounts of growth in each quadrant.

Section	Water Alone	Soap (type: _____)
1.	(No washing)	
2.		
3.		
4.		
5.		(Waterless hand cleaner)

Conclusions_____

_____

_____

Questions

1. Did your results differ from your expected results?_____

   Briefly explain why or why not. _____

2. What is a surgeon trying to accomplish with a 10-minute scrub with a brush followed by an antiseptic?

   _____

   _____

3. How do normal microbiota and transient microbiota differ? _____

   _____

4. Using your classmates' data, compare the results from bar soap and liquid soap._____

   _____

   _____

Critical Thinking

1. If most of the normal microbiota and transient microbiota aren't harmful, then why must hands be scrubbed before surgery?

2. The following data were collected from soaps after 1 week of use at a hospital nurses' handwashing station. Neither bacteria nor fungi were isolated from any of the products before use.

   Isolation of aerobic bacteria from 25 soap products. Data are expressed as percentage of soap products contaminated.

Organisms	Bar Soap	Liquid Soap: Type of Closure			
		Screw Top	Slit/Flip	Flip/Pump	Pump
Total bacteria	95%	71%	39%	10%	0%
Gram-positive cocci	95%	71%	39%	10%	0%
Gram-negative rods	12%	1%	1%	1%	0%

What conclusions can you draw from these data?

Unknown Identification and *Bergey's Manual*

The strategy of discovery lies in determining the sequence of choice of problems to solve. Now it is in fact very much more difficult to see a problem than to find a solution to it. The former requires imagination, the latter only ingenuity.

JOHN BERNAL

Objectives

After completing this exercise, you should be able to:

1. Explain how bacteria are characterized and classified.
2. Use *Bergey's Manual.*
3. Identify an unknown bacterium.

Background

In microbiology, a system of classification must be available to allow the microbiologist to categorize and classify organisms. Communication among scientists would be very limited if no universal system of classification existed. Until recently, the **taxonomy** (grouping) of bacteria was difficult because few definite anatomical or visual differences exist. With these limitations, most bacteria are identified through evaluation of primary characteristics, such as morphology and growth patterns, and secondary characteristics, such as metabolism and serology. A characteristic that is critical for distinguishing one bacterial group from another may be irrelevant for identification of other bacteria.

The most important reference for bacterial taxonomy is **Bergey's Manual,*** in which bacteria are classified according to similarities in their ribosomal RNA (rRNA). The Domains Bacteria and Archaea are included in *Bergey's Manual.* Bacteria and Archaea with similar rRNA sequences are grouped together into taxa. The taxa used for the Bacteria and Archaea are phylum, class, order, family, genus, and species. Although the characteristics of a given group are relatively constant, through repeated laboratory culture, atypical bacteria will be found. This variability, however, only heightens the fun of classifying bacteria.

You will be given an unknown heterotrophic bacterium to characterize and identify. By using careful deduction and systematically compiling and analyzing data, you should be able to identify the bacterium.

Keys to species of bacteria are provided later. These keys are an example of a dichotomous classification system—that is, a population is repeatedly divided into two parts until a description identifies a single member. Such a key is sometimes called an "artificial key" because there is no single correct way to write one. You may want to check your conclusion with the species description given in *Bergey's Manual.*

To begin your identification, ascertain the purity of the culture you have been given and prepare stock and working cultures. Avoid contamination of your unknown. Note growth characteristics and Gram-stain appearance for clues about how to proceed. After culturing and staining the unknown, many bacterial groups can be eliminated. Final determination of your unknown will depend on carefully selecting the relevant biochemical tests and weighing the value of one test over another in case of contradictions. Enjoy!

Materials

Petri plates containing Trypticase soy agar (2)

Trypticase soy agar slant (2)

All stains, reagents, and media previously used

Culture

Unknown bacterium # _____

Techniques Required

Compound light microscopy

Hanging-drop procedure

---

*Bergey's Manual of Systematic Bacteriology, 2nd ed., 5 vols. (2005), is the reference for classification. *Bergey's Manual of Determinative Bacteriology,* 9th ed. (1994), is used for laboratory identification of culturable bacteria and archaea.

Wet-mount technique

Negative staining

Gram staining

Acid-fast staining

Endospore, capsule, and flagella staining

Inoculating loop and needle technique

Aseptic technique

Plate streaking

OF test

Starch hydrolysis

MRVP tests

Fermentation tests

Citrate test

Protein catabolism

Catalase test

Nitrate reduction test

Oxidase test

Procedure

1. Streak your unknown onto the agar plates for isolation. Incubate one plate at 35°C and the other at room temperature for 24 to 48 hours. Note the growth characteristics and the temperature at which each one grows best.

2. Aseptically inoculate two Trypticase soy agar slants from a colony on your streak plate. Incubate them for 24 hours. Describe the resulting growth. Keep both slant cultures in the refrigerator. One is your stock culture; the other is your working culture. Subculture your stock culture onto another slant when your working culture is contaminated or not viable. Keep the working culture in the refrigerator when it is not in use.

3. Use your working culture for all identification procedures. When a new slant is made and its purity demonstrated, discard the old working culture. What should you do if you think your culture is contaminated? _____

_____

4. Develop ideas on how to proceed. Perhaps determining staining characteristics might be a good place to start. What shape is it? _____ What can be eliminated? _____

5. After determining its staining and morphologic characteristics, determine which biochemical tests you will need. Do not be wasteful. Inoculate *only* what is needed. It is not necessary to repeat a test—do it once accurately. Do not perform unnecessary tests.

6. If you come across a new test—one not previously done in this course—determine whether it is essential. Can you circumvent it? _____ If not, consult your instructor.

7. Record your results in the Laboratory Report and identify your unknown.

LABORATORY REPORT

Unknown Identification and *Bergey's Manual*

NAME _____

DATE _____

LAB SECTION _____

Purpose _____

_____

_____

Data

Write "not tested" (NT) next to tests that were not performed. Unknown # _____

Morphological, Staining, and Cultural Characteristics	Microscopic Examination Sketches: Label and Give Magnification (___ ×)				
The cell					
Staining characteristics					
Gram _____ Age _____					
Other _____ Age _____					
Shape _____					
Size _____					
Arrangement _____					
Endospores (position) _____	**Results: Essential Biochemical Characteristics**				
_____		Time (hr)			Temp. ___ °C
Motility _____		24	48	· ·	
Determined by _____	Glucose				
Colonies on Trypticase soy agar	Lactose				
Diameter _____	Mannitol				
Appearance _____	Catalase				
Color _____	Oxidase				Abbreviations:
Elevation _____	H₂S				A = Acid
Margin _____	Nitrate reduction				G = Gas
Consistency _____	Indole				a = slight acid
Agar slant Age _____	Methyl red				alk = alkaline
Amount of growth _____	V–P				+ = positive
Pattern _____	Citrate				− = negative
Color _____					ng = no growth

Other characteristics, special media, etc. _____

_____

_____

Conclusion

What organism was in unknown # _____ ? _____

Questions

1. On a separate sheet of paper, write your rationale for arriving at your conclusion.

2. Why is it necessary to complete the identification of a bacterium based on its physiology rather than its

    morphology? _____

    _____

    _____

    _____

3. Place the following organisms next to their description in the key shown below:

Actinomyces	*Escherichia*	*Pseudomonas*
Bacillus	*Lactobacillus*	Purple sulfur bacteria
Bacteroides	*Mycobacterium*	*Staphylococcus*
Campylobacter	*Mycoplasma*	*Streptococcus*
Clostridium	*Neisseria*	*Streptomyces*
Corynebacterium	*Nitrosomonas*	*Thiobacillus*
Cyanobacteria	*Nocardia*	*Treponema*

    I. Gram-positive

       A. Rods

          1. Produce conidiospores

             a. Aerobic   _____

             b. Anaerobic   _____

          2. Endospore-forming

             a. Obligate anaerobe   _____

             b. Facultative anaerobe   _____

          3. Nonendospore-forming

             a. Acid-fast

                (1) Mycelia formed   _____

                (2) Mycelia not formed   _____

             b. Not acid-fast

                (1) Regular   _____

                (2) Club-shaped; stain irregularly _____

B. Cocci

    1. Oxidative; catalase-positive   _____

    2. Fermentative; catalase-negative   _____

C. No cell wall   _____

II. Gram-negative

    A. Heterotrophic

        1. Helical or vibroid

            a. Possess axial filament   _____

            b. Possess flagella   _____

        2. Rods

            a. Aerobic   _____

            b. Facultatively anaerobic   _____

            c. Anaerobic   _____

        3. Cocci   _____

    B. Autotrophic

        1. Photoautotrophic

            a. Produce O_2 _____

            b. Do not produce O_2 _____

        2. Chemoautotrophic

            a. Oxidize N-containing inorganic compounds   _____

            b. Oxidize S-containing inorganic compounds   _____

Isolation and Titration of Bacteriophages

Objectives

After completing this exercise, you should be able to:

1. Isolate a bacteriophage from a natural environment.
2. Describe the cultivation of bacteriophages.
3. Determine the titer of a bacteriophage sample using the broth-clearing and plaque-forming methods.

Background

Bacteriophages, a term coined around 1917 by Félix d'Hérelle meaning "bacteria eater," parasitize most, if not all, bacteria in a very specific manner. Some bacteriophages, or **phages,** such as T-even bacteriophages, have a **complex structure** (Figure 1a). The protein coat consists of a polyhedral head and a helical tail, to which other structures are attached. The head contains the nucleic acid. To initiate an infection, the bacteriophage **adsorbs** onto the surface of a bacterial cell by means of its tail fibers and base plate. The bacteriophage injects its nucleic acid into the bacterium during **penetration** (Figure 1b). The tail sheath contracts, driving the tail core through the cell wall and injecting the nucleic acid into the bacterium.

Bacteriophages can be grown in liquid or solid cultures of bacteria. The use of solid media makes location of the bacteriophage possible by the **plaque-forming method.** Host bacteria and bacteriophages are mixed together in melted agar, which is then poured into a Petri plate containing hardened nutrient agar. Each bacteriophage that infects a bacterium multiplies, releasing several hundred new viruses. The new viruses infect other bacteria, and more new viruses are produced. All the bacteria in the area surrounding the original virus are destroyed, leaving a clear area, or **plaque,** against a confluent "lawn" of bacteria. The lawn of bacteria is produced by the growth of uninfected bacterial cells.

In this exercise, we will isolate a bacteriophage from host cells in a natural environment (i.e., in sewage or houseflies). Because the numbers of phages in a natural source are low, the desired host bacteria and additional nutrients are added as an **enrichment procedure.** After incubation, the bacteriophage can be isolated by centrifugation of the enrichment media and membrane filtration. **Filtration** has been used for removing microbes from liquids for purposes of sterilization since

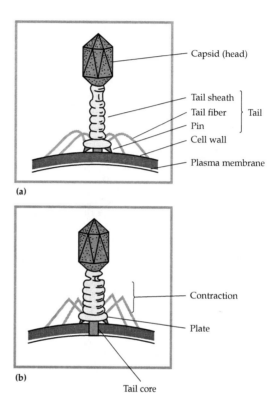

Figure 1

T-even bacteriophage. **(a)** Diagram of a bacteriophage, showing its component parts and adsorption onto a host cell. **(b)** Penetration of a host cell by the bacteriophage.

1884, when Pasteur's associate, Charles Chamberland, made the first out of porcelain. Today most filtration of viruses is done using nitrocellulose or polyvinyl membrane filters with pore sizes (usually 0.45 μm) that physically exclude bacteria from the filtrate.

You will measure the viral activity in your sample by performing sequential dilutions of the viral preparation and assaying for the presence of viruses. In the **broth-clearing assay,** the **endpoint** is the highest dilution (smallest amount of virus) producing lysis of bacteria and clearing of the broth. The **titer,** or concentration, that results in a recognizable effect is the reciprocal of the endpoint. In the plaque-forming method, the titer is determined by counting plaques. Each plaque theoretically corresponds to a single infective virus in the initial suspension. Some plaques may arise from more than one virus particle, and some virus particles may not be infectious. Therefore, the titer is determined by counting the number of **plaque-forming units (pfu).** The titer, plaque-forming units per milliliter, is determined by counting the number of plaques and dividing by the amount plated times the dilution. For example, 32 plaques with 0.1 ml plated of a 1:10³ dilution is equal to

$$\frac{32}{0.1 \times 10^{-3}} = 3.2 \times 10^5 \text{ pfu/ml}$$

In this exercise, we will determine the viral activity by a plaque-forming assay and a broth-clearing assay.

Materials

Isolation of Bacteriophage

Use flies, sewage, or bacteriophages to culture.

Flies as source:
Houseflies (fresh) (20 to 25); bring your own (Figure 2)
Trypticase soy broth (20 ml)
Mortar and pestle

Sewage as source:
Raw sewage (45 ml)
10× nutrient broth (5 ml)
50-ml graduated cylinder
Funnel

Bacteriophage as source:
Bacteriophage
Trypticase soy broth (20 ml)

Sterile 125-ml Erlenmeyer flask

Sterile 5-ml pipette (1)

Centrifuge tubes

Screw-capped tube

Sterile membrane filter (0.45 μm)

Sterile membrane filter apparatus

Safety goggles

Gloves

Titration of Bacteriophage

Tubes containing 9 ml of Trypticase soy broth (6)

Petri plates containing nutrient agar (6)

Tubes containing 3 ml of melted soft Trypticase soy agar (0.7% agar) (6)

Sterile 1-ml pipettes (7)

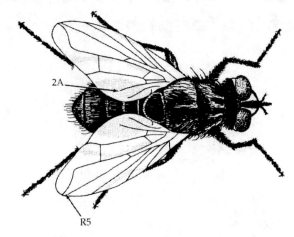

Figure 2
Houseflies may harbor bacteriophages. To identify a housefly, observe that the 2A vein doesn't reach the wing margin, and the R5 cell narrows.

Cultures

Escherichia coli broth

Bacteriophage culture or bacteriophage from isolation procedure

Techniques Required

Pour plate technique

Pipetting

Serial dilution technique

Membrane filtration

Procedure

Isolation of Bacteriophage

 Wear gloves and goggles when working with raw sewage. Handle flies carefully.

1. Follow enrichment procedure a, b, or c.
    a. Wear gloves. Add the flies to half of the Trypticase soy broth in the mortar, and grind with the pestle to a fine pulp. Transfer this mixture to a sterile flask, and add the remainder of the broth and 2 ml of *E. coli*. Place the mortar and pestle in the To Be Autoclaved basket and the gloves in the biohazard container.

b. Wear gloves and safety glasses. Add 45 ml of sewage to 5 ml of 10× nutrient broth in a sterile flask. Add 5 ml of *E. coli* broth. Mix gently. Place gloves in the biohazard container. Why is the broth 10 times more concentrated than normal? _____

c. Add 0.5 ml of bacteriophage to 20 ml of Trypticase soy broth in a sterile flask. Add 2 ml of *E. coli* broth. Mix gently.

2. Incubate the enrichment for 24 hours at 35°C.

3. Decant 10 ml of the enrichment into a centrifuge tube. Place the tube in a centrifuge.

 Balance the centrifuge with a similar tube containing 10 ml of water.

Centrifuge at 2500 rpm for 10 minutes to remove most bacteria and solid materials.

4. Filter the supernatant through a membrane filter. Decant the clear liquid into a screw-capped tube. How does filtration separate viruses from bacteria?

_____

_____

Store at 5°C until the next lab period.

Titration of Bacteriophage (Figure 3)

Read carefully before proceeding.

1. Label the plates and the broth tubes "1" through "6."

2. Aseptically add 1 ml of phage suspension (from step 4, above) to tube 1. Mix by carefully aspirating up and down three times with the pipette. Using a different pipette, transfer 1 ml to the second tube, mix well, and then put 1 ml into the third tube. Why is the pipette changed? _____
Continue until the fifth tube. After mixing this

tube, discard 1 ml into a container of disinfectant. What dilution exists in each tube?

	Tube 1	Tube 2	Tube 3
Dilutions:	_____	_____	_____

	Tube 4	Tube 5	Tube 6
Dilutions:	_____	_____	_____

What is the purpose of tube 6? _____

3. With a pipette, add 0.1 ml of *E. coli* to the soft agar tubes and place them back in the water bath. Keep the water bath at 43°C to 45°C at all times. Why?

_____

4. With the remaining pipette, start with broth tube 6 and aseptically transfer 0.1 ml from tube 6 to the soft agar tube. Mix by swirling, and quickly pour the inoculated soft agar evenly over the surface of Petri plate 6. Then, using the same pipette, transfer 0.1 ml from tube 5 to a soft agar tube, mix, and pour over plate 5. Continue until you have completed tube 1. Why can the procedure be done with one pipette? _____

_____

5. After completing step 4, add two loopfuls of *E. coli* to each of the remaining broth tubes and mix. Incubate the tubes at 35°C. Observe them in a few hours. In the broth tubes, record the highest dilution that was clear as the endpoint. The titer is the reciprocal of the endpoint.

6. Incubate the plates at 35°C until plaques develop. The plaques may be visible within hours. Plates can be stored at 5°C.

7. Select a plate with between 25 and 250 plaques. Count the number of plaques, and calculate the number of plaque-forming units (pfu) per milliliter. Record your results.

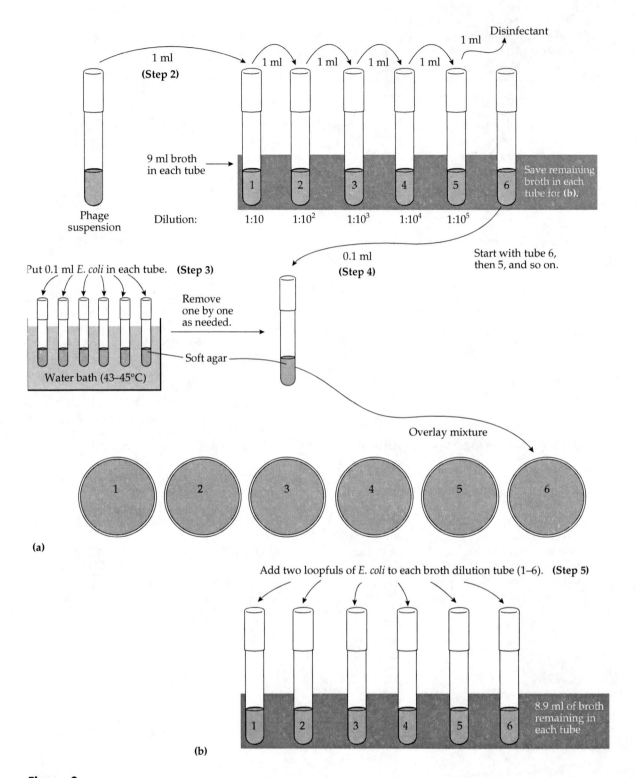

Figure 3

Procedure for titration of bacteriophages. (a) Plaque-forming assay.
(b) Broth-clearing assay.

LABORATORY REPORT

Isolation and Titration of Bacteriophages

NAME _____

DATE _____

LAB SECTION _____

Purpose _____

_____

_____

Data

Plaque-Forming Assay

Choose one plate with 25 to 250 plaques.

Draw what you observed.

    Number of plaques = _____

    Dilution used for that plate = _____

Broth-Clearing Assay

Indicate whether each tube was turbid or clear.

Incubated _____ hours.

Tube	Turbid or Clear	Dilution
1		
2		
3		
4		
5		
6		

Conclusions

Plaque-Forming Assay

pfu/ml = _____

Show your calculations.

Broth-Clearing Assay

What was the endpoint? _____

What was the titer? _____

Questions

1. Are any contaminating bacteria present? How can you tell? _____

   _____

2. Why did you add *Escherichia coli* to sewage, which is full of bacteria? _____

   _____

   _____

3. Are all the plaques the same size? Briefly explain why or why not. _____

   _____

   _____

4. What does the endpoint represent in a broth-clearing assay? _____

   _____

   _____

   _____

5. Which of these assays is more accurate? Briefly explain. _____

   _____

   _____

Critical Thinking

1. How would you develop a pure culture of a phage?

2. If there were no plaques on your plates, offer an explanation. How would you explain turbidity in all of the tubes in a broth-clearing assay?

3. How would you isolate a bacteriophage for a species of *Bacillus*?

4. Titration of a phage on a pure bacterial lawn resulted in some cloudy plaques. Briefly explain this result.

Bacteria of the Skin

Objectives

After completing this exercise, you should be able to:

1. Isolate and identify bacteria from the human skin.
2. Provide an example of normal skin microbiota.
3. List characteristics used to identify the staphylococci.
4. Explain why many bacteria are unable to grow on human skin.

Background

The skin is generally an inhospitable environment for most microorganisms. The dry layers of keratin-containing cells that make up the epidermis (the outermost layer of the skin) are not easily colonized by most microbes. Sebum, secreted by oil glands, inhibits bacterial growth, and salts in perspiration create a hypertonic environment. Perspiration and sebum are nutritive for certain microorganisms, however, which establishes them as part of the normal microbiota of the skin.

Normal microbiota of the skin tend to be resistant to drying and to relatively high salt concentrations. More bacteria are found in moist areas, such as the axilla (armpit) and the sides of the nose, than on the dry surfaces of arms or legs. Transient microbiota are present on hands and arms in contact with the environment.

Propionibacterium live in hair follicles on sebum from oil glands. The propionic acid they produce maintains the pH of the skin between 3 and 5, which suppresses the growth of other bacteria. Most bacteria on the skin are gram-positive and salt-tolerant.

Staphylococcus aureus is part of the normal microbiota of the skin and is also considered a pathogen. S. *aureus*, which produces **coagulase,** an enzyme that coagulates (clots) the fibrin in blood, is pathogenic. A test for the presence of coagulase is used to distinguish S. *aureus* from other species of *Staphylococcus*.

Although many different bacterial genera live on human skin, in this exercise we will attempt to isolate and identify a catalase-positive, gram-positive coccus.

Materials

Petri plate containing mannitol salt agar

Sterile cotton swab

Sterile saline

Second Period

Petri plate containing mannitol salt agar

3% hydrogen peroxide

Gram-staining reagents

Fermentation tubes

Coagulase plasma (as needed)

Toothpick

Techniques Required

Gram staining

Plate streaking

Selective media

Fermentation tests

Catalase test

Procedure

1. Wet the swab with saline, and push the swab against the wall of the test tube to express excess saline (Figure 1a). Swab any surface of your skin. The sides of the nose, axilla, an elbow, or a pus-filled sore are possible areas.
2. Swab one-third of the plate with the swab.

 Discard the swab in disinfectant.

Using a sterile loop, streak back and forth into the swabbed area a few times, and then streak away from the inoculum (Figure 1b), to cover about one-third of the agar. Sterilize your loop and spread the bacteria over the rest of the agar.

3. Incubate the plate, inverted, at 35°C for 24 to 48 hours.
4. Examine the colonies. Record the appearance of the colonies and any mannitol fermentation (yellow halos). Perform a Gram stain of the colonies and test for catalase production. Perform the catalase test by making a suspension of the

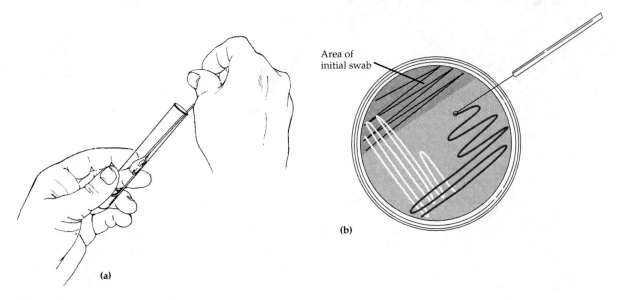

Figure 1

Taking a sample from the skin. **(a)** Aseptically moisten a sterile cotton swab in saline.
(b) After swabbing half the plate, use a sterile loop to streak the inoculum over the
agar.

desired colony on a slide with a toothpick and
adding a drop of H_2O_2. Discard the toothpick in
the biohazard container.

5. Subculture a catalase-positive, gram-positive coccus
    on another mannitol salt plate. Do not attempt to
    subculture a colony that has not been tested for
    catalase. Why? _____

6. Identify your isolate.
    a. To test for coagulase, place a loopful of rehy-
        drated coagulase plasma on a clean slide. Add
        a loopful of water and make a heavy suspen-
        sion of the bacteria to be tested. Observe for
        clumping of the bacterial cells (clumping =
        coagulase-positive; no clumping = coagulase-
        negative).
    b. Inoculate the appropriate fermentation tubes.
        Incubate the fermentation tubes at 35°C for 24
        to 48 hours.

Bacteria of the Skin

NAME _____

DATE _____

LAB SECTION _____

Purpose _____

_____

_____

Data

Source of inoculum: _____

First Mannitol Salt Plate

Colony			
	1	2	3
Colony description			
Pigment			
Mannitol fermentation			

Which colony was isolated? _____

Catalase reaction: _____

Gram stain

Reaction: _____

Morphology: _____

Arrangement: _____

Additional Biochemical Tests

_____

_____

_____

Conclusion

What organism did you identify? _____

Questions

1. Why is mannitol salt agar used as a selective medium for normal skin microbiota? _____

   _____

   _____

2. After you have observed a gram-positive coccus, what is the additional information you need before perform-

   ing a coagulase test? _____

3. List three identifying characteristics of *Staphylococcus aureus*. _____

   _____

   _____

4. List three factors that protect the skin from infection. _____

   _____

   _____

   _____

Critical Thinking

1. What is coagulase? How is it related to pathogenicity?

2. Assume that you isolated *S. aureus* from your skin. How would you determine whether it was penicillin-resistant?

3. An 8-year-old male went to the pediatrician complaining of pain in his right hip. He had no previous injury to the hip or leg. His temperature was 38°C. A bone scan revealed damage to the head of the femur. Bacterial cultures of blood and fluid from the hip joint were positive for a gram-positive, catalase-positive, coagulase-positive cocci that ferment mannitol. Use Appendix H to identify the species of this bacterium.

Bacteria of the Respiratory Tract

Objectives

After completing this exercise, you should be able to:

1. List representative normal microbiota of the respiratory tract.
2. Differentiate the pathogenic streptococci based on biochemical testing.

Background

The respiratory tract can be divided into two systems: the upper and lower respiratory tracts. The **upper respiratory tract** consists of the nose and throat, and the **lower respiratory tract** consists of the larynx, trachea, bronchial tubes, and alveoli. The lower respiratory tract is normally sterile because of the efficient functioning of the ciliary escalator. The upper respiratory tract is in contact with the air we breathe—air contaminated with microorganisms.

The throat is a moist, warm environment, allowing many bacteria to establish residence. Species of many different genera—such as *Staphylococcus, Streptococcus, Neisseria,* and *Haemophilus*—can be found living as normal microbiota in the throat. Despite the presence of potentially pathogenic bacteria in the upper respiratory tract, the rate of infection is minimized by microbial **antagonism.** Certain microorganisms of the normal microbiota suppress the growth of other microorganisms through competition for nutrients and production of inhibitory substances.

Streptococcal species are the predominant organisms in throat cultures, and some species are the major cause of bacterial sore throats (acute pharyngitis). Streptococci are identified by biochemical characteristics, including hemolytic reactions, and antigenic characteristics (Lancefield's system). Hemolytic reactions are based on hemolysins that are produced by streptococci while growing on blood-enriched agar. Blood agar is usually made with defibrinated sheep blood (5.0%), sodium chloride (0.5%) to minimize spontaneous hemolysis, and nutrient agar. Three patterns of hemolysis can occur on blood agar:

1. **Beta-hemolysis:** Complete hemolysis, giving a clear zone with a clean edge around the colony.

2. **Alpha-hemolysis:** Green, cloudy zone around the colony. Partial destruction of red blood cells due to bacteria-produced hydrogen peroxide.
3. **Gamma-hemolysis:** No hemolysis, and no change in the blood agar around the colony.

Streptococci that are alpha-hemolytic and gamma-hemolytic are usually normal microbiota, whereas beta-hemolytic streptococci are frequently pathogens.

The streptococci can be antigenically classified into Lancefield groups A through O by antigens in their cell walls. Over 90% of streptococcal infections are caused by beta-hemolytic group A streptococci. These bacteria are assigned to the species *S. pyogenes. S. pyogenes* is sensitive to the antibiotic bacitracin; other streptococci are resistant to bacitracin Optochin sensitivity is used to distinguish pathogenic *S. pneumoniae* from other alpha-hemolytic streptococci.

Materials
Throat Culture

Petri plate containing blood agar

Sterile cotton swab

Gram-staining reagents

Toothpicks

Hydrogen peroxide, 3% (second period)

Streptococcus

Petri plate containing blood agar

Sterile cotton swabs (2)

Forceps and alcohol

Optochin disk

Bacitracin disk

10% bile salts (second period)

Tubes containing 2 ml of nutrient broth (2) (second period)

Cultures

Streptococcus pyogenes

Streptococcus pneumoniae

Techniques Required

Gram staining

Plate streaking

Catalase test

Kirby-Bauer technique

Procedure

Throat Culture

 Work only with swabs collected from your own throat.

1. Swab your throat with a sterile cotton swab. The area to be swabbed is between the "golden arches" (glossopalatine arches), as shown in Figure 1. Do not hit the tongue.
2. After obtaining an inoculum from the throat, swab one-half of a blood agar plate. Streak the remainder of the plate with a sterile loop.

 Discard the swab in disinfectant.

3. Incubate the plate, inverted, at 35°C for 24 hours. Observe the plate for hemolysis. Transfer some colonies to a slide with a toothpick, and perform a catalase test. Discard the toothpick in the biohazard container. Why can't the catalase test be done on blood agar? _____

_____

_____

Streptococcus

1. Inoculate each half of a blood agar plate, one side with S. *pyogenes* and the other half with S. *pneumoniae*. Use swabs to obtain confluent growth.

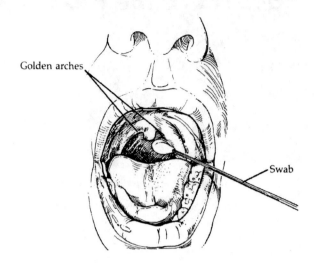

Figure 1
Swab your throat with a sterile swab.

_____

 Be careful—these bacteria are pathogens.

2. Dip forceps in alcohol and burn off the alcohol.

⚠ Keep the forceps tip pointed down while burning. Keep the beaker of alcohol away from the flame.

Using the forceps, place and press a bacitracin disk and an optochin disk on each half. Space the disks so that zones of inhibition may be observed.
3. Incubate the plates, inverted, at 35°C for 24 hours. Observe for hemolysis and inhibition of growth by bacitracin and optochin.
4. Prepare Gram stains from smears of each organism. Do the organisms differ microscopically? _____

_____

5. Using a sterile loop, prepare a suspension of each organism in a tube of nutrient broth.
6. Add a few drops of 10% bile salts to each tube. Observe the tubes after 15 minutes for lysis of the cells. Which culture is "bile soluble"? _____

Bacteria of the Respiratory Tract

NAME _____

DATE _____

LAB SECTION _____

Purpose _____

_____

_____

Data

Throat Culture

	Colony			
	1	2	3	4
Appearance of colonies on blood agar				
Hemolysis				
Catalase reaction				

Streptococcus

	Organism	
	S. pyogenes	S. pneumoniae
Gram stain		
Gram reaction		
Morphology		
Arrangement		
Blood agar plate		
Appearance of colonies		
Hemolysis		

	Organism	
	S. pyogenes	*S. pneumoniae*
Inhibition by Optochin		
Bacitracin		
Bile solubility		

Questions

1. Is blood agar selective or differential? _____ Briefly explain. _____

   _____

2. Why does addition of a bacitracin disk to a blood agar plate make a rapid identification technique?

   _____

   _____

3. Is the Gram stain of significant importance in the identification of the organisms studied in this exercise?

   Explain. _____

   _____

   _____

4. You have isolated a gram-positive coccus from a throat culture that you cannot identify as staphylococci or streptococci. A test for one enzyme can be used to distinguish *quickly* between these bacteria. What is the enzyme?

   _____

Critical Thinking

1. A 45-year-old male was admitted to the hospital with chest and back pain. On examination, his chest was dull to percussion. A chest X ray shows lower left lung infiltrates. A sputum culture reveals alpha-hemolytic, gram-positive, catalase-negative cocci that were inhibited by optochin. The bacteria produce acid from lactose. Use Appendix H to identify the species of this bacterium.

2. Assume that you isolated non–acid-fast, gram-positive, catalase-positive rods from your throat. Does this represent a disease state? Briefly explain.

Bacteria of the Urogenital Tract

Objectives

After completing this exercise, you should be able to:

1. List bacteria found in urine from a healthy individual.
2. Identify, through biochemical testing, bacteria commonly associated with urinary tract infections.
3. Determine the presence or absence of *Neisseria gonorrhoeae* in a GC smear.

Background

The urinary and genital systems are closely related anatomically, and some diseases that affect one system also affect the other system, especially in the female. The upper urinary tract and urinary bladder are usually sterile. The urethra does contain resident bacteria, including *Streptococcus, Bacteroides, Mycobacterium, Neisseria,* and enterics. Most bacteria in urine are the result of contamination by skin microbiota during passage. The presence of bacteria in urine is not considered an indication of urinary tract infection unless there are ≥1000 bacteria of one species or ≥100 coliforms per milliliter of urine.

Many infections of the urinary tract, such as cystitis (inflammation of the urinary bladder) or pyelonephritis (inflammation of the kidney), are caused by opportunistic pathogens and are related to fecal contamination of the urethra and to medical procedures, such as catheterization.

Standard examination of urine consists of a plate count on blood agar for the total number of organisms, coupled with a streak plate of undiluted urine on MacConkey agar. Why? _____

_____

The patient is given a sterile container and instructed to collect a midstream sample, which is obtained by voiding a small volume from the bladder before collection. This washes away skin microbiota.

In the first part of this exercise, you will examine normal urine. In the second part, three gram-negative rods that commonly cause cystitis will be provided to you. *E. coli* and *Proteus* are enterics. *E. coli* is one of the coliforms. What is a coliform? _____

_____

Proteus is actively motile and exhibits "swarming" on solid media where the cells at the periphery move away from the main colony. *Pseudomonas* is a gram-negative aerobic rod. *Pseudomonas aeruginosa* is commonly found in the soil and other environments. Under the right conditions, particularly in weakened hosts, this organism can cause urinary tract infections, burn and wound infections, and abscesses. *P. aeruginosa* infections are characterized by blue-green pus. This bacterium produces an extracellular, water-soluble pigment called **pyocyanin** ("blue pus") that diffuses into its growth medium.

Most diseases of the genital system are transmitted by sexual activity and are therefore called **sexually transmitted diseases (STDs).** Most of the bacterial diseases can be readily cured with antibiotics if treated early and can largely be prevented by the use of condoms. Nevertheless, STDs are a major U.S. public health problem.

The most common reportable communicable disease in the United States is gonorrhea, an STD caused by the gram-negative diplococci *Neisseria gonorrhoeae,* also called gonococci or GC. Gonorrhea is diagnosed by identifying the organism in the pus-filled discharges of patients, as demonstrated with GC smears in the third part of this exercise. Cultures from patients' discharges can be made on Thayer–Martin medium and incubated in a CO_2 jar. An oxidase test is performed on characteristic colonies for confirmation.

Materials

Urine Culture

Sterile widemouthed jar, approximately 50 to 250 ml

Petri plate containing blood agar

Petri plate containing MacConkey agar

Sterile 10-μl calibrated loops (2)

Cystitis

Petri plate containing MacConkey agar

Petri plate containing Pseudomonas agar P

Tubes containing OF-glucose medium (4)

Urea agar slants (2)

Mineral oil

Oxidase reagent (second period)

Gram-stain reagents (second period)

Cultures

Tube containing *Escherichia coli*, *Proteus vulgaris*, and *Pseudomonas aeruginosa*

GC Smears

GC smears

One unknown smear # _____

Techniques Required

Gram staining

Plate streaking

Fermentation tests

Urea hydrolysis

Oxidase test

MacConkey agar

Procedure

Urine Culture

 Work only with urine collected from your own body.

1. Collect a "clean-catch" urine specimen, as described by your instructor, using the sterile jars available in the lab. Refrigerate the specimen until you are ready to perform step 2. Why? _____

    _____

2. Gently shake the urine to suspend the bacteria. Using a 10-µl calibrated loop, streak one line down the center of the blood agar. Then streak back and forth, perpendicular to that line. *Discard the loop in disinfectant.* What volume of urine did you put on the agar? _____

3. Using another 10-µl loop, repeat step 2 to inoculate the MacConkey agar. *Discard the loop in disinfectant.*

 Discard the jar and pipettes in the appropriate biohazard container.

4. Incubate both plates, inverted, at 35°C for 24 to 48 hours.

5. Count the colonies on the blood agar plate, and determine the number of colony-forming units (cfu) per milliliter of urine:

$$\text{cfu/ml} = \frac{\text{Number of colonies}}{\text{Amount plated}}$$

6. Repeat step 5 to determine the cfu/ml on the MacConkey agar plate. Examine the MacConkey plate for the presence of possible coliforms. Consult your instructor if you are alarmed by your results.

Cystitis

1. Inoculate a MacConkey plate and Pseudomonas agar P plate with the mixed culture of bacteria.

2. Incubate the plates, inverted, at 35°C for 24 to 48 hours.

3. Examine the MacConkey plate for lactose-fermenting colonies. Which of the three organisms ferments lactose? _____
    Look for swarming. Which organism is actively motile on solid media? _____
    Are any small, nonlactose-fermenting colonies present? _____

4. Prepare a Gram stain from each different colony type.

5. Examine the Pseudomonas agar P plate. Can you identify *Pseudomonas*? _____

6. Perform an oxidase test on each different organism.

7. Inoculate four tubes of OF-glucose medium: two with *Proteus* and two with *Pseudomonas*. Plug one tube of each organism with mineral oil. Inoculate a urea agar slant with each organism. Incubate the tubes at 35°C for 24 to 48 hours.

8. Record the results of the OF-glucose and urease production tests. Why isn't it necessary to perform these two biochemical tests on *E. coli*? _____

    _____

GC Smears

1. Examine the GC smears provided.

2. Determine whether *N. gonorrhoeae* could be present in your unknown GC smear.

LABORATORY REPORT

Bacteria of the Urogenital Tract

NAME _____

DATE _____

LAB SECTION _____

Purpose _____

_____

Data

Urine Culture

	Blood Agar	MacConkey Agar
Number of colonies		
Total count (cfu/ml)		
Hemolysis		
Possible coliforms present		
How can you identify coliforms?		

Cystitis

	Organism		
	E. coli	P. vulgaris	P. aeruginosa
MacConkey agar			
Appearance of colonies	_____	_____	_____
Lactose fermentation	_____	_____	_____
Swarming	_____	_____	_____
Gram stain	_____	_____	_____
Pseudomonas agar P			
Appearance of colonies	_____	_____	_____
Pigmentation	_____	_____	_____
Oxidase reaction	_____	_____	_____
OF-glucose (fermentative or oxidative)	_____	_____	_____
Urease production	_____	_____	_____

GC Smears

Diagram the appearance of
a known GC-positive smear.

Diagram the appearance of
a known GC-negative smear.

Unknown # _____
Diagram the appearance of
your unknown smear.

_____ ×

_____ ×

_____ ×

Could *N. gonorrhoeae* be
present? _____

Questions

1. Why is MacConkey agar inoculated with a urine specimen? _____

    _____

    _____

2. With the results obtained on the blood agar and MacConkey agar plates, is a urinary tract disease possible?

    _____

3. The enterics and pseudomonads look alike microscopically. How can you easily distinguish between these two

    groups of bacteria? _____

    _____

    _____

4. Why are females more prone to urinary tract infections than males? _____

    _____

    _____

Critical Thinking

1. Differentiate between the pigment of *P. aeruginosa* on Pseudomonas agar P and the "pigment" of *E. coli* on MacConkey agar without referring to the colors.

2. What role does antibiotic treatment have in yeast infections of the urinary tract?

3. An otherwise healthy 22-year-old female was seen at a hospital emergency room because of frequent and painful urination. A urine culture reveals a gram-negative, lactose-positive rod that produces indole but no H_2S. Use Appendix H to identify the genus of this bacterium.

Microbes in Water: Multiple-Tube Technique

Objectives

After completing this exercise, you should be able to:

1. Define coliform.
2. Provide the rationale for determining the presence of coliforms.
3. List and explain each step in the multiple-tube technique.

Background

Tests that determine the bacteriological quality of water have been developed to prevent transmission of waterborne diseases of fecal origin. However, it is not practical to look for pathogens in water supplies because pathogens occur in such small numbers that they might be missed by sampling. Moreover, when pathogens are detected, it is usually too late to prevent occurrence of the disease. Rather, the presence of **indicator organisms** is used to detect fecal contamination of water. An indicator organism must be present in human feces in large numbers and must be easy to detect. The most frequently used indicator organisms are the coliform bacteria. **Coliforms** are aerobic or facultatively anaerobic, gram-negative, nonendospore-forming, rod-shaped bacteria that ferment lactose with acid and gas formation within 48 hours at 35°C. Coliforms are not usually pathogenic although they can cause opportunistic infections. Coliforms are not restricted to the human gastrointestinal tract but may be found in other animals and in the soil. Tests that determine the presence of fecal coliforms (of human origin) have been developed. The IMViC tests historically were used to distinguish coliforms of fecal origin, such as *Escherichia coli*, from other coliforms found in plants and soil.

Established public health standards specify the maximum number of coliforms allowable in each 100 ml of water, depending on the intended use of the water (for example, water for drinking or water-contact sports or treated wastewater for irrigation or for discharge into a bay or river).

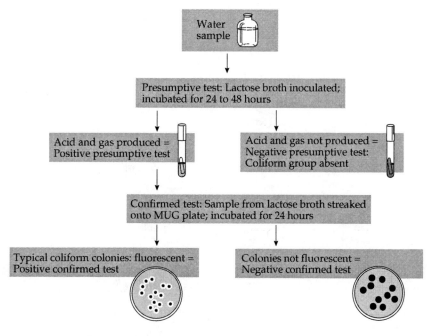

Figure 1

Analysis of drinking water for coliforms by the multiple-tube technique.

From *Laboratory Experiments in Microbiology*, Eighth Edition, Ted R. Johnson and Christine L. Case. Copyright © 2006 by Pearson Education, Inc. Published by Benjamin Cummings, Inc. All rights reserved.

Table 1

Most Probable Number (MPN) Index for Various Combinations of Positive and Negative Results When Three 10-ml Portions, Three 1-ml Portions, and Three 0.1-ml Portions Are Used

Number of Tubes Giving Positive Reaction Out of			MPN Index per 100 ml	Number of Tubes Giving Positive Reaction Out of			MPN Index per 100 ml
3 of 10 ml Each	3 of 1 ml Each	3 of 0.1 ml Each		3 of 10 ml Each	3 of 1 ml Each	3 of 0.1 ml Each	
0	0	0	<3	3	0	0	23
0	0	1	3	3	0	1	39
0	1	0	3	3	0	2	64
1	0	0	4	3	1	0	43
1	0	1	7	3	1	1	75
1	1	0	7	3	1	2	120
1	1	1	11	3	2	0	93
1	2	0	11	3	2	1	150
2	0	0	9	3	2	2	210
2	0	1	14	3	3	0	240
2	1	0	15	3	3	1	460
2	1	1	20	3	3	2	1,100
2	2	0	21	3	3	3	≥2,400
2	2	1	28				

Source: Standard Methods for the Examination of Water and Wastewater, 13th ed. New York: American Public Health Association, 1971.

Coliforms can be detected and enumerated in the **multiple-tube technique** (Figure 1). In this method, coliforms are detected in two stages. In the **presumptive test,** dilutions from a water sample are added to lactose fermentation tubes. The lactose broth can be made selective for gram-negative bacteria by the addition of lauryl sulfate or brilliant green and bile. Fermentation of lactose to gas is a positive reaction.

Samples from the positive presumptive tube at the highest dilution are examined for coliforms by inoculating a differential medium in the **confirmed test.** A confirmed test can be done on **MUG agar.** Almost all strains of *E. coli* produce the enzyme β-glucuronidase (GUD). If *E. coli* is added to a nutrient medium containing 4-methylumbelliferone glucuronide (MUG), GUD converts MUG to a fluorescent compound that is visible with an ultraviolet lamp.

The number of coliforms is determined by a statistical estimation called the **most probable number**

(MPN) method. In the presumptive test, tubes of lactose broth are inoculated with samples of the water being tested. A count of the number of tubes showing acid and gas is then taken, and then is compared to statistical tables such as the one shown in Table 1. The MPN number is *the most probable number* of coliforms per 100 ml of water.

Materials

Water sample, 50 ml (Bring your own from a pond or stream.)

9-ml, single-strength lactose fermentation tubes (6)

20-ml, 1.5-strength lactose fermentation tubes (3)

Sterile 10-ml pipette

Sterile 1-ml pipette

Petri plate containing MUG agar (second period)

Techniques Required

Aseptic technique

Plate streaking

Fermentation tests

Pipetting

Procedure

1. Label three single-strength lactose broth tubes "0.1," label another three tubes "1," and label the three 1.5-strength broth tubes "10."
2. Inoculate each 0.1 tube with 0.1 ml of your water sample.
3. Inoculate each 1 tube with 1.0 ml of your water sample.
4. Inoculate each 10 tube with 10 ml of the water sample. Why is 1.5-strength lactose broth used for this step? _____

_____

5. Incubate the tubes for 24 to 48 hours at 35°C.
6. Record the results of your presumptive test (Figure 1). Which tube has the highest dilution of the water sample? _____

_____

Determine the number of coliforms per 100 ml of the original sample using Table 1. If a tube has gas, streak the MUG agar with the positive broth. Incubate the plate, inverted, for 24 to 48 hours at 35°C.

7. Examine the plate using an ultraviolet lamp.

 Do not look directly at the ultraviolet light, and do not leave your hand exposed to it.

Record the results of your confirmed test (Figure 1). How can you tell whether coliform colonies are present? _____

_____

Microbes in Water: Multiple-Tube Technique

NAME _____

DATE _____

LAB SECTION _____

Purpose _____

_____

_____

Data

Water sample source: _____

Presumptive Test

Results	Number of Tubes with a Positive Result		
	Inoculum		
	10 ml	1 ml	0.1 ml
Growth			
Acid			
Gas			
Number of tubes positive for all 3			

Possible coliforms present? _____   MPN: _____

Confirmed Test

Tube: _____ Growth: _____

Appearance of colonies with white light: _____

_____

Appearance of colonies with UV light: _____

Are coliforms present? _____

Data from water samples tested by other students:

Sample	Coliforms Present	MPN

Conclusions

What is the MPN of your water sample? _____ per _____ ml

Questions

1. Could the water have a high concentration of the pathogenic bacterium *Vibrio cholerae* and give negative results in the multiple-tube technique? Briefly explain. _____

_____

_____

2. Why are coliforms used as indicator organisms if they are not usually pathogens? _____

_____

3. Why isn't a pH indicator needed in the lactose broth fermentation tubes? _____

_____

4. If coliforms are found in a water sample, the IMViC tests will help determine whether the coliforms are of fecal origin and not from plants or soil. What IMViC results would indicate the presence of fecal coliforms? _____

_____

_____

_____

Critical Thinking

1. Why didn't we inoculate MUG agar directly and bypass lactose broth?

2. The following table lists the etiologies of illness associated with drinking and recreational waters in 1998.

Agent	Number of Cases
Cryptosporidium hominis	936
Pseudomonas aeruginosa dermatitis	393
Norovirus	106
Escherichia coli O157:H7	9
Giardia intestinalis	2

Which of the water samples would have shown a high coliform count?

Which diseases could have been prevented by chlorinating the water?

3. Use the data shown below to explain how waterborne diseases can best be eliminated.

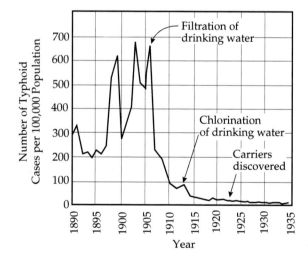

Microbes in Food: Contamination

Objectives

After completing this exercise, you should be able to:

1. Determine the approximate number of bacteria in a food sample using a standard plate count.
2. Provide reasons for monitoring the bacteriologic quality of foods.
3. Explain why the standard plate count is used in food quality control.

Background

Illness and food spoilage can result from microbial growth in foods. The sanitary control of food quality is concerned with testing foods for the presence of pathogens. During processing (grinding, washing, and packaging), food may be contaminated with soil microbes and microbiota from animals, food handlers, and machinery.

Foods are the primary vehicle responsible for the transmission of diseases of the digestive system. For this reason, they are examined for the presence of coliforms because the presence of coliforms usually indicates fecal contamination.

Standard plate counts are routinely performed on food and milk by food-processing companies and public health agencies. The **standard plate count** is used to determine the total number of viable bacteria in a food sample. The presence of large numbers of bacteria is undesirable in most foods because it increases the likelihood that pathogens will be present, and it increases the potential for food spoilage.

In a standard plate count, the number of **colony-forming units (cfu)** is determined. Each colony may arise from a group of cells rather than from one individual cell. The initial sample is diluted through serial dilutions (Appendix B) in order to obtain a small number of colonies on each plate. A known volume of the diluted sample is placed in a sterile Petri dish and melted cooled nutrient agar is poured over the inoculum. After incubation, the number of colonies is counted. Plates with between 25 and 250 colonies are suitable for counting. A plate with fewer than 25 colonies is unsuitable for counting because a single contaminant could influence the results. A plate with more than 250 colonies is extremely difficult to count.

The microbial population in the original food sample can then be calculated using the following equation:

Colony-forming units/gram or ml of sample =

$$\frac{\text{Number of colonies}}{\text{Amount plated} \times \text{dilution*}}$$

A limitation of the standard plate count is that only bacteria capable of growing in the culture medium and environmental conditions provided will be counted. A medium that supports the growth of most heterotrophic bacteria is used.

Materials

Melted standard plate count or nutrient agar, cooled to 45°C

Sterile 1-ml pipettes (8)

Sterile Petri dishes (10)

Sterile weighing dish

Sterile spatula

Sterile 99-ml dilution blanks (3)

Sterile 9-ml dilution blanks (2)

Food samples

Vortex mixer

Techniques Required

Aseptic technique

Pour-plate technique

Pipetting

Serial dilution technique

---

*"Dilution" refers to the tube prepared by serial dilutions (Appendix B). For example, if 250 colonies were present on the 1:10^6 plate, the calculation would be as follows:

$$\begin{aligned}
\text{Colony-forming units/gram} &= \frac{250 \text{ colonies}}{0.1 \text{ ml} \times 10^{-5}} \\
&= 250 \times 10^5 \times 10^1 \\
&= 250{,}000{,}000 \\
&= 2.5 \times 10^8
\end{aligned}$$

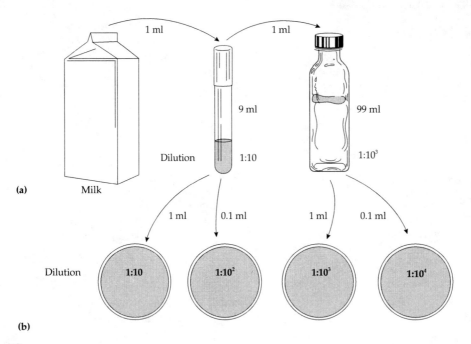

Figure 1

Standard plate count of milk. **(a)** Make serial dilutions of a milk sample. **(b)** Mark four Petri dishes with the dilutions.

Procedure

First Period. A: Bacteriologic Examination of Milk

1. Obtain a sample of either raw or pasteurized milk.
2. Using a sterile 1-ml pipette, aseptically transfer 1 ml of the milk into a 9-ml dilution blank; label the tube "1:10" and discard the pipette (Figure 1a). Mix the contents of the tube on a vortex mixer.
3. Using a sterile 1-ml pipette, aseptically transfer 1 ml of the 1:10 dilution into a 99-ml dilution blank; label the bottle "$1:10^3$" and discard the pipette. Shake the bottle 20 times, with your elbow resting on the table, as shown in Figure 2.
4. Label the bottoms of four sterile Petri dishes with the dilutions: "1:10," "$1:10^2$," "$1:10^3$," and "$1:10^4$" (Figure 1b).
5. Using a 1-ml pipette, aseptically transfer 0.1 ml of the $1:10^3$ dilution into the bottom of the $1:10^4$ dish. *Note:* 0.1 ml of the $1:10^3$ dilution results in a $1:10^4$ dilution of the original sample. Using the same pipette, transfer 1.0 ml of the $1:10^3$ dilution into the dish labeled $1:10^3$. Pipette 0.1 ml and 1.0 ml from the 1:10 dilution into the $1:10^2$ and 1:10 dishes, respectively, with the same pipette (Figure 3a). Why is it important to proceed from the highest to the lowest dilution?_____

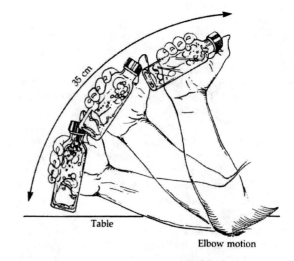

Figure 2

Shake the dilution bottle 20 times through a 35-cm arc.

6. Check the temperature of the water bath containing the nutrient agar. Test the temperature of the outside of the agar container with your hand. It should be "baby bottle" warm. Why?_____

7. Pour the melted nutrient agar into one of the dishes (to about one-third full) (Figure 3b). Cover the plate and swirl it gently (Figure 3c) to distribute

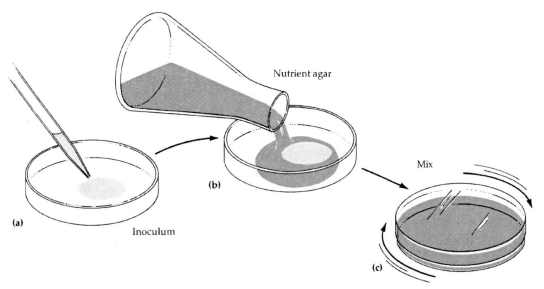

Figure 3

Pour plate. (a) Pipette inoculum into a Petri dish. (b) Add liquefied nutrient agar, and (c) mix the agar with the inoculum by gently swirling the plate.

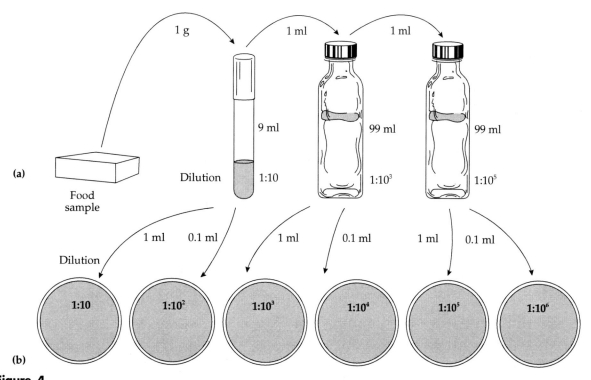

Figure 4

Standard plate count on food. (a) Prepare serial dilutions of a food sample. (b) Label six Petri dishes with the dilutions to be plated.

the milk sample evenly through the agar. Continue until all the plates are poured.

8. When each plate has solidified, invert it, and incubate all plates at 35°C for 24 to 48 hours.

First Period. B: Bacteriologic Examination of Hamburger or Hot Dog and Frozen Vegetables

1. Weigh 1 g of raw hamburger (or hot dog) or frozen, thawed vegetables by using the sterile spatula and weighing dish.

2. Transfer the 1 g of food into a 9-ml dilution blank; label the tube "1:10" (Figure 4a). Mix the contents on a vortex mixer. Mixing will shake bacteria off the food and put them in suspension.

3. Using a sterile 1-ml pipette, aseptically transfer 1 ml of the 1:10 dilution into a 99-ml dilution blank; label the bottle "1:10^3" and discard the pipette. Shake the bottle 20 times, with your elbow resting on the table, as shown in Figure 2. Make a 1:10^5 dilution using another 99-ml dilution blank. Shake the bottle as before.

4. Label the bottoms of six sterile Petri dishes with the dilutions: " 1:10," "1:10^2," "1:10^3," "1:10^4," "1:10^5," and "1:10^6" (Figure 4b).

5. Using a 1-ml pipette, aseptically transfer 0.1 ml of the 1:10^5 dilution into the 1:10^6 dish. *Note:* 0.1 ml of a 1:10^5 dilution results in a 1:10^6 dilution of the original sample. Using the same pipette, repeat this procedure with the 1:10^3 dilution and the 1:10 dilution until all the dishes have been inoculated (Figure 3a). Why can the same pipette be used for each transfer? _____

_____

_____

6. Check the temperature of the water bath containing the nutrient agar. Test the temperature of the outside of the agar container with your hand. It should be "baby bottle" warm. Why? _____

_____

7. Pour the melted nutrient agar into one of the dishes (to about one-third full) (Figure 3b). Cover the plate and swirl it gently (Figure 3c) to distribute the sample through the agar evenly. Continue until all the plates are poured.

8. When each plate has solidified, invert it, and incubate all plates at 35°C for 24 to 48 hours.

Second Period

1. Arrange each plate in order from lowest to highest dilution.

2. Select the plate with 25 to 250 colonies. Record data for plates with fewer than 25 colonies as *too few to count (TFTC)* and those with more than 250 colonies, *too numerous to count (TNTC)*.

3. Count the number of colonies on the plate selected.

4. Calculate the number of bacteria in the original food. For example, if 129 colonies were counted on a 1:10^3 dilution:

$$\frac{129 \text{ colonies}}{1 \text{ ml} \times 10^{-3}} = 129{,}000$$
$$= 1.29 \times 10^5 \text{ colony-forming units/ml or gram of milk or food}$$

Microbes in Food: Contamination

NAME _____

DATE _____

LAB SECTION _____

Purpose _____

_____

_____

Data

Milk sample: _____

Dilution	Colonies per Plate
1:	
1:	
1:	
1:	

Number of colony-forming units per ml of original milk sample: _____

Make your calculations in the space below.

Food sample: _____

Dilution	Colonies per Plate
1:	
1:	
1:	
1:	
1:	
1:	

Number of colony-forming units per gram of original food: _____

Make your calculations in the space below.

Record data for other foods tested by other students.

Food	cfu/ml (or gram)

Questions

1. What could you do to ensure that the bacteria present in foods do not pose a health hazard? _____

   _____

   _____

2. Why are plates with 25 to 250 colonies used for calculations? _____

   _____

   _____

3. In a quality-control laboratory, each dilution is plated in duplicate or triplicate. Why would this increase the
   accuracy of a standard plate count? _____

   _____

   _____

4. There are other techniques for counting bacteria, such as a direct microscopic count and turbidity. Why is the
   standard plate count preferred for food? _____

   _____

   _____

5. Why is ground beef a better bacterial growth medium than a steak or roast? _____

   _____

6. Why does repeated freezing and thawing increase bacterial growth in meat? _____

   _____

Critical Thinking

1. Assume that a standard plate count indicates that a substantial number of microbes are present in the food sample. What should be done next to determine whether the food sample is a danger to the consumer?

2. Pasteurized milk is allowed 20,000 cfu/ml. How many colonies would be present if 1 ml of a 10^{-3} dilution was

   plated? _____ Is 20,000 cfu/ml a health hazard? _____

3. An outbreak of botulism associated with home-canned chili peppers killed 16 members of one family. Would a standard plate count have detected the etiologic agent in the canned chili peppers? Briefly explain.

Epidemiology

Objectives

After completing this exercise, you should be able to:

1. Define the following terms: epidemiology, epidemic, reservoir, and carrier.
2. Describe three methods of transmission.
3. Define index case and case definition.
4. Determine the source of a simulated epidemic.

Background

In every infectious disease, the disease-producing microorganism, the **pathogen,** must come in contact with the **host,** the organism that harbors the pathogen. **Communicable diseases** can be spread either directly or indirectly from one host to another. Some microorganisms cause disease only if the body is weakened or if a predisposing event such as a wound allows them to enter the body. Such diseases are called **noncommunicable diseases**—that is, they cannot be transmitted from one host to another. The science that deals with when and where diseases occur and how they are transmitted in the human population is called **epidemiology. Endemic diseases** such as pneumonia are constantly present in the population. When many people in a given area acquire the disease in a relatively short period of time, it is referred to as an **epidemic disease.** The first reported patient in a disease outbreak is the **index case.** One of the first steps in analyzing a disease outbreak is to make a **case definition,** which should include the typical symptoms of patients so you know who should be included.

Diseases can be transmitted by **direct contact** between hosts. **Droplet infection,** when microorganisms are carried on liquid drops from a cough or sneeze, is a method of direct contact. Diseases can also be transmitted by contact with contaminated inanimate objects, or **fomites.** Drinking glasses, bedding, and towels are examples of fomites that can be contaminated with pathogens from feces, sputum, or pus.

Some diseases are transmitted from one host to another by vectors. **Vectors** are insects and other arthropods that carry pathogens. In **mechanical transmission,** insects carry a pathogen on their feet and may transfer the pathogen to a person's food. For example, houseflies may transmit typhoid fever from the feces of an infected person to food. Transmission of a disease by an arthropod's bite is called **biological transmission.** An arthropod ingests a pathogen while biting an infected host. The pathogen can multiply or mature in the arthropod and then be transferred to a healthy person in the arthropod's feces or saliva.

The continual source of an infection is called the **reservoir.** Humans who harbor pathogens but who do not exhibit any signs of disease are called **carriers.**

An **epidemiologist** compiles data on the incidence of a disease and its method of transmission and tries to locate the source of infection in order to decrease the incidence. The time course of an epidemic is shown by graphing the number of cases and their date of onset. This **epidemic curve** gives a visual display of the outbreak's magnitude and time trend. An epidemic curve provides a great deal of information. First, you will usually be able to tell where you are in the course of the epidemic and possibly be able to project its future course. Second, if you have identified the disease and know its usual incubation period, you may be able to estimate a probable time period of exposure and can then develop a questionnaire focusing on that time period. Finally, you may be able to draw inferences about the epidemic pattern, for example, whether it is an outbreak resulting from a common-source exposure, from a person-to-person spread, or both.

In this exercise, an epidemic will be simulated. Although you will be in the "epidemic," you will be the epidemiologist who, by deductive reasoning and with luck, determines the source of the epidemic.

Materials

Petri plate containing nutrient agar

Latex or vinyl glove, or small plastic sandwich bag

One unknown swab per student (one swab has *Serratia marcescens, Rhodotorula rubra,* or *Micrococcus roseus* on it. Your instructor will tell you which organism.)

Techniques Required

Colony morphology

Procedure (Figure 1)

1. Divide the Petri plate into five sectors, labeled "1" through "5."
2. Record the number of your swab in your Lab Report.

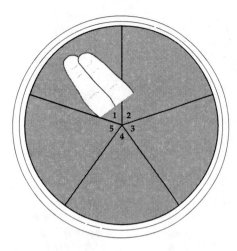

Figure 40.1

After touching the palm of one classmate with your gloved fingers, immediately touch sector 1 of the plate. Record the person's name and swab number. After the finger–palm touch with a second classmate, touch sector 2. Continue until you have inoculated all five sectors.

Carefully read steps 3 through 9 before proceeding.

3. Put a glove on your left hand. Carefully unwrap your swab without touching the cotton. Holding the swab with your right hand, rub it on the palm of your left hand (i.e., on the glove).

4. Discard the swab in a container of disinfectant.

5. Using your gloved left hand, touch the gloved palm of a classmate when the instructor gives the signal. Your gloved fingers touch the other's gloved palm and vice versa.

6. After the finger–palm touch, touch your fingers to the first sector of the nutrient agar. Record the person's name and swab number.

7. Repeat the finger–palm touch with a different classmate. Then touch your fingers to the second sector of the nutrient agar. Record the person's name and swab number.

8. Repeat steps 5 and 6, doing the finger–palm touch with another classmate and then touching the third sector of the nutrient agar.

9. Repeat steps 5 and 6, doing the finger–palm touch with two other classmates. Remember to touch your fingers to the corresponding sector of the nutrient agar after each handshake. Keep good records.

10. Discard the glove in the To Be Autoclaved basket.

11. Incubate the plate, inverted, at room temperature.

12. At the next lab period, record your results. Data can be keyed into a computer database. Using your group's data, deductively try to determine who had the contaminated fomite.

Epidemiology

NAME _____

DATE _____

LAB SECTION _____

Purpose _____

_____

_____

Data

Your swab # _____ Which organism was on the contaminated swab? _____

What is the case definition for this classroom "epidemic"? _____

_____

Sector	Student's Name	Swab Number	Appearance of Colonies on Nutrient Agar
1.			
2.			
3.			
4.			
5.			

Attach your group's or the class's data.

Conclusions

1. Who was the index case (the contaminated swab)? _____

2. What number was the contaminated swab? _____ Explain how you arrived at your conclusion.

_____

3. Diagram the path of the epidemic from the index case to all "infected" class members.

Questions

1. Could you be the "infected" individual and not have growth on your plate? Explain. _____

    _____

    _____

    _____

2. Do all people who contact an infected individual acquire the disease? _____

    _____

    _____

    _____

3. How can an epidemic stop without medical intervention (e.g., quaratine, chemotherapy, vaccines)?

    _____

    _____

    _____

4. Are any organisms other than the culture assigned for this experiment growing on the plates? How can you tell?

    _____

    _____

    _____

5. What was the method of transmission of the "disease" in this experiment?_____

    _____

    _____

    _____

Critical Thinking

1. Assume you work in the Infectious Disease Branch of the Centers for Disease Control and Prevention. You are notified of the following two incidents. (1) On June 20, cruise ship X reported that 84 of 2,318 passengers had reported to the infirmary with norovirus gastroenteritis during a 7-day vacation cruise. According to federal regulations, when the incidence of acute gastroenteritis among passengers and crew exceeds 3%, an outbreak is defined and requires a formal investigation. Is this an outbreak? _____ (2) A nursing home reported 125 cases of norovirus gastroenteritis among residents and staff during the week of June 23rd.

   Data collected from the cruise ship and nursing home are shown in the following table. Use these data to answer the questions.

	Cruise Ship Data		Nursing Home Data	
	Date	Number of Cases	Date	Number of Cases
Cruise one	6/9	2	6/23	1
	6/10	4	6/24	8
	6/11	5	6/25	12
	6/12	3	6/26	12
	6/13	3	6/27	50
	6/14	2	6/28	32
	6/15	1	6/29	10
Cruise two	6/16	2	6/30	8
	6/17	10		
	6/18	13		
	6/19	13		
	6/20	84		
	6/21	46		
	6/22	20		
Cruise three	6/23	10		
	6/24	23		
	6/25	39		
	6/26	41		
	6/27	18		
	6/28	17		
	6/29	9		

   a. Graph the epidemic curve for these data.

   b. How is norovirus transmitted?

   c.   What happened on cruise 2?

   d.   What would you do before cruise 4?

   e.   Three nursing home residents were passengers on cruise 2. What can you conclude?

2.   During a 3-month period, acute hepatitis B virus (HBV) infection was diagnosed in nine residents of a nursing home. Serological testing of all residents revealed that nine people had acute HBV infection, two had chronic infection, five were immune, and 58 were susceptible. Medical charts of residents were reviewed for history of medications and use of ancillary medical services. Infection-control practices at the nursing home were assessed through interviews with personnel and direct observations of nursing procedures. A summary of the medical charts is shown below.

	Case Patients*	Susceptible Residents†
Received insulin injections	11	58
Patients having capillary blood taken by fingersticks	11	6
≥60 fingersticks/month	7	0
<60 fingersticks/month	4	6
Average number of venous blood draws/month	23	6
Patients having both capillary and venous blood drawn	11	39
Visited by dentist	1	5
Visited by podiatrist	10	52
Recieved blood transfusion	0	0

*A case patient has hepatitis B.
† Susceptible residents live in the nursing home but do not have hepatitis B.

   a.   What is the usual method of transmission for hepatitis B? _____

   b.   What is the probable source of infection in hospitals? _____

   c.   How was *this* infection transmitted? _____

   _____

   _____

3. A health department received a report from hospital A that 15 patients had been admitted on October 12 with unexplained pneumonia. On October 21, hospital B, located 15 miles from hospital A, reported a higher-than-normal pneumonia census for the first 2 weeks of October. *Legionella pneumophila* was eventually identified in 23 patients, 21 were hospitalized, and two died. To identify potential exposures associated with *L. pneumophila*, a questionnaire was developed, and a case-control study was initiated on November 2 to identify the source of infection. Three healthy controls were selected for each confirmed case; controls were matched by age, gender, and underlying medical conditions. Of the 15 case patients for whom a history was available, 14 had visited a large home improvement center 2 weeks before onset of illness. Results of the questionnaire are shown below.

	Case Patients	Healthy Controls
Number of patients	15	45
Visited home improvement center	14	12
Average time at center (min)	79	29
Looked at whirlpool spa X	13	9
Looked at whirlpool spa Y	13	1
Visited greenhouse sprinkler system display	10	10
Visited decorative fish pond	14	12
Used drinking fountain	13	10
Used urinals	10	4
Used restroom hot water	6	4
Used restroom cold water	8	8

a. What is the most likely source of this outbreak of legionellosis? _____

b. How would you prove this was the source?

c. How was this disease transmitted?

d. Provide an explanation of the infected patient who did not go to the home improvement center.

4. A salmonellosis outbreak occurred after a brunch in Livonia, New York. All fresh food items were delivered to the cooking area the morning of May 22. The menu consisted of omelets, bacon, fruit salad, and pastries.

Omelets consisted of grade A eggs from a Maryland farm. They were beaten and mixed with milk, salt, pepper, and diced onions. The egg batter was fried in small batches and served from warming trays heated by alcohol burners.

Bacon was purchased from a meat wholesaler. The bacon was fried on a large griddle and served from warming trays.

Fruit salad was made from fresh apples, bananas, and oranges; they were cut up and mixed with commercially canned peaches and pears.

Muffins and other breads were purchased from a bakery and served with butter.

Case	Foods Eaten*				Beverages†	Time of Meal	Symptoms‡	Onset of Symptoms	
	1	2	3	4				Day	Hr
1	x	x	x	x	C, J	1100	D, V, N, A	Sun	2400
2		x	x	x	M, J	1200			
3	x	x	x	x	C	1200	N, A	Mon	0200
4	x	x	x	x	C	1200	D, N, A	Mon	0600
5				x	T	1100			
6		x		x	C, J	1200			
7			x	x	C, J	1300			
8				x	C, J	1300			
9	x	x	x	x	C	1100	D, V, N, A	Mon	1100
10				x	T	1200			
11				x	M	1300			
12	x	x	x	x	M	1300	D, N, A	Mon	1400
13				x	C	1200			
14		x	x	x	C, J	1500			
15	x	x		x	T	1500	D, N, V	Mon	2400
16				x	M, J	1100			
17		x	x	x	C	1100			
18		x		x	C	1200	N	Sun	1300
19	x	x			T	1200	D, V, N, A	Mon	1700
20			x	x	C, J	1200			
21	x	x		x	M	1300	D, N, A	Mon	0200
22				x	M	1400	A	Tues	0800
23				x	M, J	1400			
24	x	x	x	x	C	1100	D, A	Mon	1500
25	x	x		x	C	1100	V, N, A	Mon	1100
26			x	x	T	1200			
27				x	T	1100			
28	x	x	x	x	C	1200	D, A	Mon	0200
29		x		x	M	1300			
30					C, J	1400			
31		x	x		C	1100			
32	x	x	x	x		1200	D, A	Mon	1200

*Foods Eaten: 1, omelet; 2, bacon; 3, fruit salad; 4, pastry.
†Beverages: C, coffee; T, tea; M, milk; J, orange juice.
‡Symptoms: D, diarrhea; N, nausea; V, vomiting; A, abdominal cramps.

a. What was the source of this disease? _____

b. How could this outbreak have been prevented? _____

Appendix:

Dilution Techniques and Calculations*

Bacteria, under good growing conditions, will multiply into such large populations that it is often necessary to dilute them to isolate single colonies or to obtain estimates of their numbers. This requires mixing a small, accurately measured sample with a large volume of sterile water or saline, which is called the **diluent** or **dilution blank.** Accurate dilutions of a sample are obtained through the use of pipettes. For convenience, dilutions are usually made in multiples of 10.

A single dilution is calculated as follows:

$$\text{Dilution} = \frac{\text{Volume of the sample}}{\text{Total (volume of the sample + the diluent)}}$$

For example, the dilution of 1 ml into 9 ml equals

$$\frac{1}{1 + 9} \text{ , which is } \frac{1}{10} \text{ and is written 1:10}$$

The same formula applies for all dilutions, regardless of the volumes. A dilution of 0.1 ml into 0.9 ml equals

$$\frac{0.1}{0.1 + 0.9} \text{ , which is } \frac{0.1}{1} = \frac{1}{10} = 1:10$$

A dilution of 0.5 ml into 4.5 ml equals

$$\frac{0.5}{0.5 + 4.5} \text{ , which is } \frac{0.5}{5.0} = \frac{1}{10} = 1:10$$

Experience has shown that better accuracy is obtained with very large dilutions if the total dilution is made out of a series of smaller dilutions rather than one large dilution. This series is called a **serial dilution,** and the total dilution is the product of each dilution in the series. For example, if 1 ml is diluted with 9 ml, and then 1 ml of that dilution is put into a second 9-ml diluent, the final dilution will be

$$\frac{1}{10} \times \frac{1}{10} = \frac{1}{100} \text{ or 1:100}$$

To facilitate calculations, the dilution is written in exponential notation. In the example above, the final dilution 1:100 would be written 10^{-2}. Remember,

$$1:100 = \frac{1}{100} = 0.01 = 10^{-2}$$

A serial dilution is illustrated in Figure 1.

*Adapted from C. W. Brady. "Dilutions and Dilution Calculations." Unpublished paper. Whitewater, WI: University of Wisconsin, n.d.

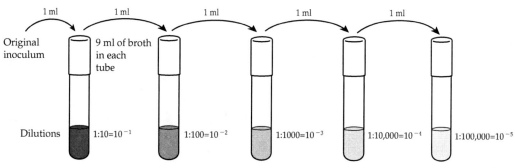

Figure 1

A 1-ml sample from the first tube will contain 1/10 the number of cells present in 1 ml of the original sample. A 1-ml sample from the last tube will contain 1/100,000 the number of cells present in 1 ml of the original sample.

Twofold dilutions are commonly used to dilute patient's serum to measure antibodies. The same formula applies: a dilution of 100 μl of sample into 100 μl of saline equals

$$\frac{100}{100 + 100} \text{, which is } \frac{100}{200} = \frac{1}{2} = 1:2$$

If 100 μl of this 1:2 dilution is put in 100 μl of saline, the final dilution is

$$\frac{1}{2} \times \frac{1}{2} = \frac{1}{4}$$

Procedure

1. Aseptically pipette 1 ml of sample into a dilution blank.
    a. If the dilution is into a tube, mix the contents on a vortex mixer or by rolling the tube back and forth between your hands.
    b. If the dilution is into a 99-ml blank, hold the cap in place with your index finger and shake the bottle up and down through a 35-cm arc
2. It is necessary to use a fresh pipette for each dilution in a series, but it is permissible to use the same pipette to remove several samples from the same bottle, as when plating out samples from a series of dilutions.

Problems

Practice calculating serial dilutions using the following problems.

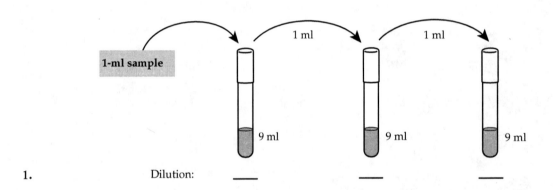

1.   Dilution: ____   ____   ____

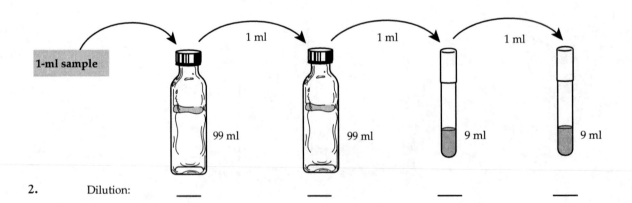

2.   Dilution: ____   ____   ____   ____

3. Design a serial dilution to achieve a final dilution of 10^{-8}.

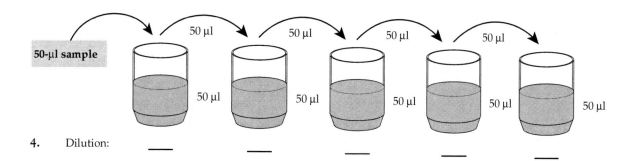

50-μl sample

50 μl   50 μl   50 μl   50 μl

50 μl   50 μl   50 μl   50 μl   50 μl

4. Dilution: _____   _____   _____   _____   _____

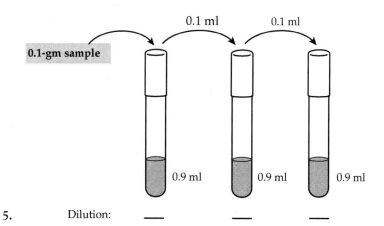

0.1-gm sample

0.1 ml   0.1 ml

0.9 ml   0.9 ml   0.9 ml

5. Dilution: _____   _____   _____

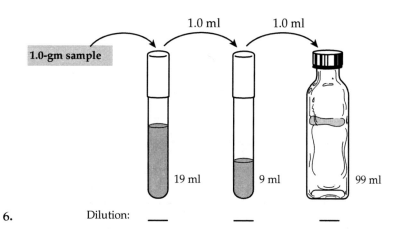

1.0-gm sample

1.0 ml   1.0 ml

19 ml   9 ml   99 ml

6. Dilution: _____   _____   _____

Exponents, Exponential Notation, and Logarithms*

Very large and very small numbers—such as 4,650,000,000 and 0.00000032—are cumbersome to work with. It is more convenient to express such numbers in exponential notation—that is, as a power of 10. For example, 4.65×10^9 is written in **standard exponential notation,** or **scientific notation;** 4.65 is the **coefficient,** and 9 is the power, or **exponent.** In standard exponential notation, the coefficient is a number between 1 and 10, and the exponent is a positive or negative number.

To change a number into exponential notation, follow two steps. First, determine the coefficient by moving the decimal point so you leave only one nonzero digit to the left of it. For example:

$$0.00000032$$

The coefficient is 3.2. Second, determine the exponent by counting the number of places you moved the decimal point. If you moved it to the left, the exponent is a positive number. If you moved it to the right, the exponent is negative. In the example, you moved the decimal point 7 places to the right, so the exponent is -7. Thus

$$0.00000032 = 3.2 \times 10^{-7}$$

Now suppose we are working with a very large number instead of a very small number. The same rules apply, but our exponential value will be positive rather than negative. For example:

$$4,650,000,000 = 4.65 \times 10^{+9}$$

$$= 4.65 \times 10^9$$

To multiply numbers written in exponential notation, multiply the coefficients and *add* the exponents. For example:

$$(3 \times 10^4) \times (2 \times 10^3) =$$
$$(3 \times 2) \times 10^{4\,+\,3} = 6 \times 10^7$$

To divide numbers written in exponential notation, divide the coefficients and *subtract* the exponents. For example:

$$\frac{3 \times 10^4}{2 \times 10^3} = \frac{3}{2} \times 10^{4\,-\,3} = 1.5 \times 10^1$$

Microbiologists use exponential notation in many kinds of situations. For instance, exponential notation is used to describe the number of microorganisms in a population. Such numbers are often very large. Another application of exponential notation is to express concentrations of chemicals in a solution—chemicals such as media components, disinfectants, or antibiotics. Such numbers are often very small. Converting from one unit of measurement to another in the metric system requires multiplying or dividing by a power of 10, which is easiest to carry out in exponential notation.

A **logarithm** is the power to which a base number is raised to produce a given number. Usually we work with logarithms to the base 10, abbreviated $\log_{10}$. The first step in finding the $\log_{10}$ of a number is to write the number in standard exponential notation. If the coefficient is exactly 1, the $\log_{10}$ is simply equal to the exponent. For example:

$$\log_{10} 0.00001 = \log_{10}(1 \times 10^{-5})$$
$$= -5$$

If the coefficient is not 1, as is often the case, a calculator must be used to determine the logarithm.

Microbiologists use logs for pH calculations and for graphing the growth of microbial populations in culture.

---

*Source: G. J. Tortora, B. R. Funke, and C. L. Case. *Microbiology: An Introduction,* 9th ed. San Francisco, CA: Benjamin Cummings, 2007, Appendix D.

Appendix:

Keys to Bacteria

This appendix deals with the identification of bacteria. The information is arranged in **dichotomous keys.** In a dichotomous key, identification is based on successive questions, each of which has two possible answers (*di-* means two). After answering each question, the investigator is directed to another question until an organism is identified. There is no single "correct" way to write a key; the goal is to conclude with one unambiguous identification.

1	Selected gram-positive heterotrophic bacteria
2	Selected gram-negative heterotrophic bacteria
3	Gram-positive cocci commonly found on human skin
4	Streptotococci found in the mouth
5	Identification of enteric genera primarily using MacConkey agar and TSI
6	Enterococci commonly found in the human intestine

222

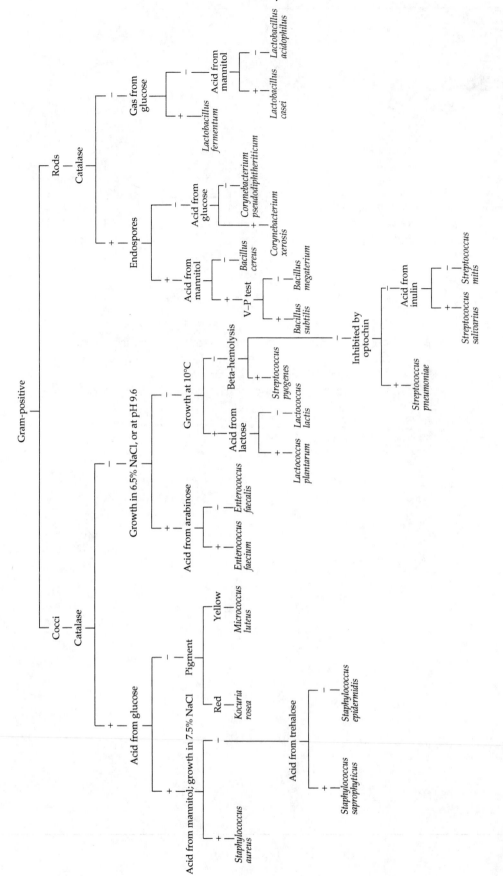

Figure 1

Key to selected gram-positive heterotrophic bacteria.

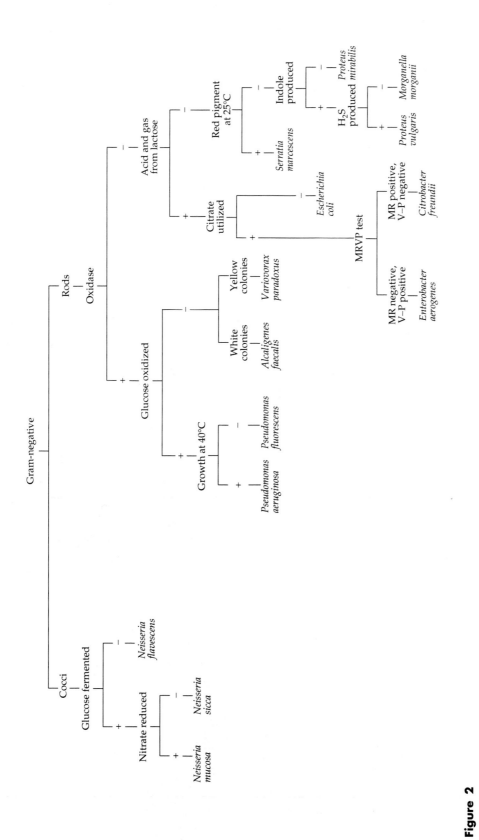

Figure 2

Key to selected gram-negative heterotrophic bacteria.

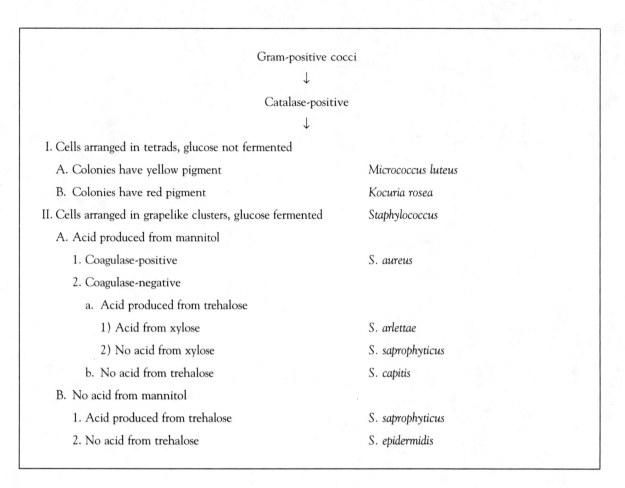

Figure 3

Key to gram-positive cocci commonly found on human skin.

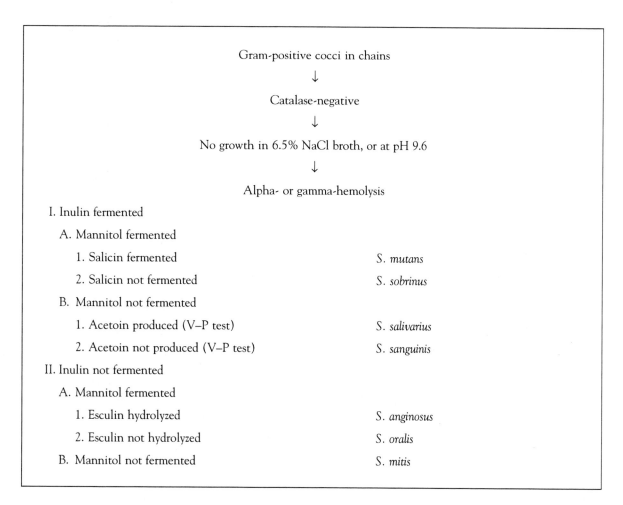

Figure 4

Key to streptococci found in the mouth.

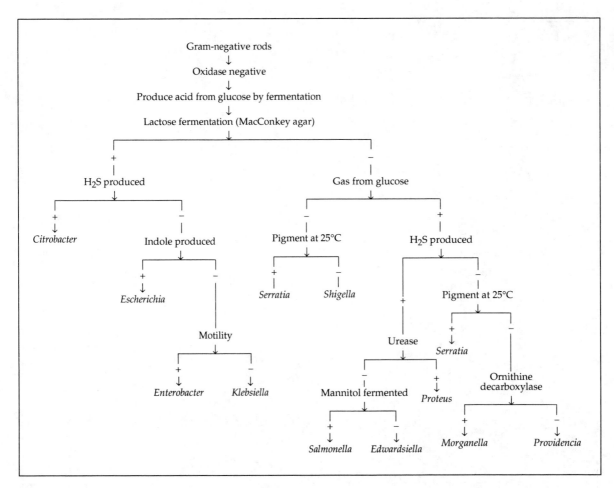

Figure 5

Identification scheme for enteric genera primarily using MacConkey agar and TSI.

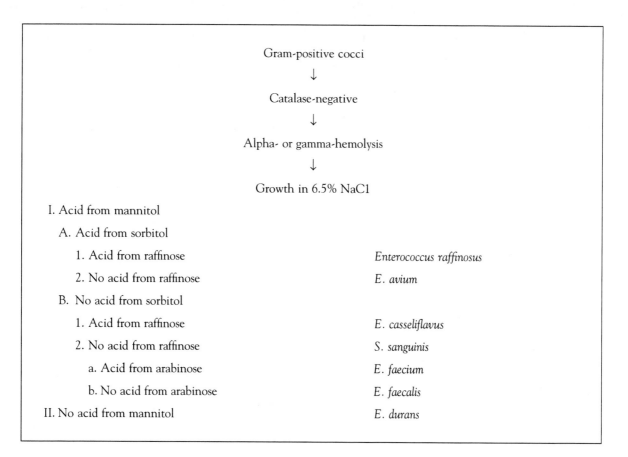

Gram-positive cocci
↓
Catalase-negative
↓
Alpha- or gamma-hemolysis
↓
Growth in 6.5% NaCl

I. Acid from mannitol
  A. Acid from sorbitol
    1. Acid from raffinose   *Enterococcus raffinosus*
    2. No acid from raffinose   *E. avium*
  B. No acid from sorbitol
    1. Acid from raffinose   *E. casseliflavus*
    2. No acid from raffinose   *S. sanguinis*
      a. Acid from arabinose   *E. faecium*
      b. No acid from arabinose   *E. faecalis*
II. No acid from mannitol   *E. durans*

Figure 6

Key to enterococci commonly found in the human intestine.

Appendix:

Pipetting

Pipettes are used for measuring small volumes of fluid. They are usually coded according to the total volume and graduation units (Figure 1). To fill a pipette, use a bulb or other mechanical device, as shown in Figure 2.

 Never use your mouth to fill a pipette.

Draw the desired amount of fluid into the pipette. Read the volume at the bottom of the meniscus (Figure 3). Fill the pipette to above the zero mark, and then allow it to drain just to the zero. The desired amount can then be dispensed.

Microbiologists use two types of pipettes. The **serological pipette** is meant to be emptied to deliver the total volume (Figure 4a). Note that the graduations stop above the tip. The **measuring pipette** delivers the volume read on the graduations (Figure 4b). This pipette is not emptied, but the flow must be stopped when the meniscus reaches the desired level.

Aseptic use of a pipette is often required in microbiology. Bring the entire closed pipette container to your work area. Lay down the canister, as shown in Figure 5. If the pipettes are wrapped in paper, open the wrapper at the end opposite the delivery end; in a canister, the delivery end will be at the bottom of the canister. Do not touch the delivery end of a sterile pipette. Remove a pipette, attach the pipette aspirator, and with your other hand, pick up the sample to be pipetted. Remove the cap from the sample with the little finger of the hand holding the pipette. Fill the pipette, and replace the cap on the sample.

 After pipetting, place the contaminated pipette in the appropriate container of disinfectant. If it is a disposable pipette, discard it in a biohazard bag or any container designated for biohazards.

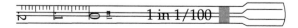

Figure 1

This pipette holds a total volume of 1 ml when filled to the zero mark. It is graduated in 0.01-ml units.

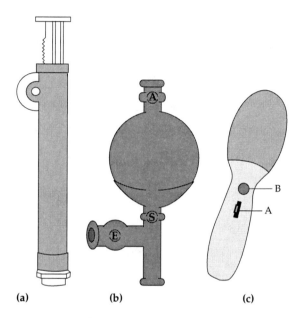

(a)   (b)   (c)

Figure 2

Three types of pipette aspirators. **(a)** Attach this plastic pump to the pipette, and turn the wheel to draw fluid into the pipette. Turning the wheel in the other direction will release the fluid. **(b)** Insert a pipette into this bulb. While pressing the A valve, squeeze the bulb, and it will remain collapsed. To draw fluid into the pipette, press the S valve; to release fluid, press the E valve. **(c)** Insert a pipette into the stem. Raise the lever **(A)** to draw fluid up; lower the lever to release the fluid. Pushing the button **(B)** will release the last drop.

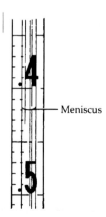

Figure 3

Read the fluid volume at the lowest level of the meniscus.

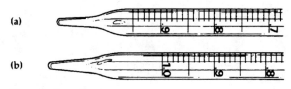

(a)

(b)

Figure 4

(a) A serological pipette. (b) A measuring pipette.

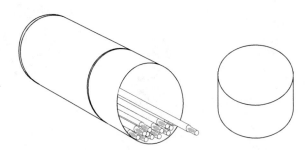

Figure 5

Proper placement of a pipette canister.

Micropipettes are used to measure volumes of less than 1 ml. The design and operation of micropipettes vary according to the manufacturer. Most use a disposable tip to hold the fluid, as shown in Figure 6. To use a micropipette, select one that holds the volume you need. The micropipette is labeled with its range—for example, 0.5–10 μl, 1–10 μl, 10–100 μl, 100–1000 μl. Set the desired volume on the digital display (Figure 7a) by turning the control knob (Figure 7b).

Questions

1.   Which micropipette would you use to measure 15 μl?

2.   If this is the display for the micropipette you chose for question 1, write in the 1 and 5 to show 15 μl.

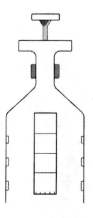

3.   How do you eject the tip on your micropipette?

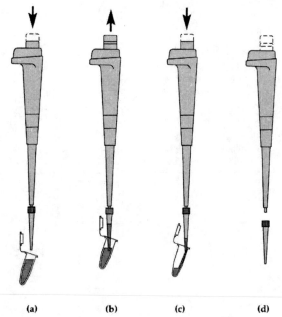

(a)   **(b)**   **(c)**   **(d)**

Figure 6

Generalized use of a micropipette. (a) Depress the control button, and insert the tip into the liquid. (b) Smoothly release the button to allow the liquid to enter the tip. (c) Place the tip against the inside of the receiving tube, and depress the button. (d) Eject the used tip by pressing the eject button or by pressing the control button to the final stop.

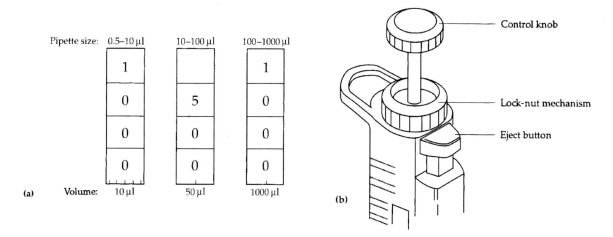

Figure 7

Adjusting a micropipette. **(a)** Reading the display. **(b)** Turning the control knob on this micropipette changes the volume picked up when the control knob is depressed.